The Great
Drug
Deception

The Great Drug Deception

THE SHOCKING STORY OF MER/29
and the Folks Who Gave You Thalidomide

RALPH ADAM FINE

STEIN AND DAY / *Publishers* / New York

First published in 1972
Copyright © 1972 by Ralph Adam Fine
Library of Congress Catalog Card No. 76-187302
All rights reserved
Published simultaneously in Canada by Saunders of Toronto Ltd.
Designed by Bernard Schleifer
Printed in the United States of America
Stein and Day/*Publishers*/7 East 48 Street, New York, N.Y. 10017
ISBN 8128-1470-3

To Charles Sopkin, with thanks; my parents;
Burt and Brenda; the Pranges;
and, of course, Kay

Contents

This book is a report on the development and sale of the drug known as MER/29, and its aftermath, as reflected in numerous judicial proceedings and Congressional investigations. It is based upon the sworn testimony introduced in such proceedings and investigations, as well as the extensive documentation submitted in connection therewith, and the official reports thereof.

1

The Squashed Bug

There is a story, possibly apocryphal, about the eighteenth-century Swedish botanist Linnaeus, who after having spent many years studying and classifying plant life turned his attention to animals with the special hope of proving his theory, then widely believed, that each creature was specially and divinely created. One day, however, while walking through his garden the great naturalist spied an unusual-looking spindly green insect crawling through the tall grass. Instantly Linnaeus' trained scientific eye recognized that the tiny invertebrate was the living disproof of his cherished theory. His hands trembled and his brow glistened with the perspiration of indecision. He took a halting breath; and then walked on, first crushing the insect into the moist earth with the heel of his shoe. Linnaeus smelled the sweet succulence of his garden and tried to force the unpleasant truth from his mind.

Linnaeus' decision to squash the bug came to mind when I read the reply of a scientist formerly employed by the Wm. S. Merrell Co., the makers of MER/29, to a question put to him by that company's attorney. He was asked whether in the course of his employment at Merrell he had ever been requested to change a scientific report. He answered that on one occasion, when he first joined the company, his superior wanted him to smooth out a "big drop in one graph" because he "wanted to publish the data, and he didn't think it would look good to show this drop." While this incident did not concern MER/29, it, and the anecdote about Linnaeus, illustrates what can happen when a scientist exchanges his traditional (and I believe sacred) role of impartial reporter of observed phenomena for that of advocate. Unfortunately too many scientists who work for drug companies are advocates. MER/29 is, in large measure, their story. It is the story of many squashed bugs.

2

MER/29—An Overview

The Wm. S. Merrell Company was founded in 1828 by William Stanley Merrell, a thirty-year-old druggist who had just recently moved to Cincinnati, Ohio. In the early years his firm sold a variety of patent medicines that were then popular, but as time passed Merrell began to make his own products. An adherent of eclectic medicine, he specialized in the production of herbal medicines; one of his most successful lines was alcoholic plant extracts known as Green Drug Preparations. Eventually, especially after William Merrell died in 1880, the company deemphasized its eclectic line and moved into more traditional areas.

While remaining essentially a family-run business, Merrell continued to expand its research, manufacturing, and sales facilities until in 1938 it had over two hundred employees (excluding salesmen) and a recognized list of pharmaceutical products. In that year the company was purchased by the Vick Chemical Company (manufacturers of the famous Vick's Vapo Rub) and until 1960 was run as a wholly owned subsidiary corporation of Vick. In 1960 the name of the Vick Chemical Company was changed to Richardson-Merrell, Inc., and in a simultaneous reorganization Merrell's separate corporate entity was eliminated and it became a division of Richardson-Merrell. The Wm. S. Merrell division continues to be headquartered in Cincinnati, the adopted home of its founder over 140 year ago. In September of 1971, it was merged into another of Richardson-Merrell's many divisions, The National Drug Company. The resulting entity is now known as Merrell-National Laboratories.

As part of its continuing research program, Merrell in the early 1950s was searching for an agent which would effectively lower cholesterol levels in humans and thus alleviate, it was widely thought, atherosclerosis (a form of hardening of the arteries or arteriosclerosis), an ailment which kills or disables millions of Americans each year. Atherosclerosis occurs when deposits of fatty substances coat the inside of the arterial walls narrowing the affected arteries and causing them to lose their natural elasticity. This forces the heart to strain in order to maintain an effective supply of blood throughout the body. Additionally, in some places the blood will tend to clot around a fatty deposit, further narrowing the arterial opening. Occasionally the blood clot or a lump of the fatty substance itself will break off into the bloodstream and be carried like a piece of flotsam through the arterial system until it reaches a point where the artery is too narrow to let it pass further. There it will stop, blocking the blood flow and causing the cells served by the plugged artery to die. If this blockage occurs in an artery feeding the brain, the person suffers a stroke. If it occurs in an artery nourishing the heart muscles, he suffers a heart attack.

The human heart is a most remarkable organ. It pumps more than four thousand gallons of blood each day, through more than sixty thousand miles of blood vessels. In the larger arteries the blood will reach speeds exceeding forty miles per hour. The heart works continuously, resting for a mere fraction of a second between each of the forty million powerful contractions it makes every year. It is an engineering marvel that man has not yet been able to come even close to duplicating. But the heart is also extremely sensitive; it needs a constant supply of oxygen or it will die. If an artery supplying it with oxygen should become clogged with material which impedes the free flow of blood, the heart will be damaged, often irreparably. The terrifying stabbing chest pains known as angina pectoris are nature's warning that the heart is not receiving enough oxygen. Prolonged oxygen starvation caused either by a partially clogged artery or one which is totally blocked (called a coronary occlusion—a coronary thrombosis occurs when the blockage or "occlusion" is caused by a blood clot) results in the death of the affected heart muscle cells. This destruction of heart muscle is known as myocardial infarction and can interfere with the heart's ability to function normally. Heart disease is the nation's number-one killer, and atherosclerosis is a major cause of heart disease.

Since it has been statistically demonstrated that persons with high cholesterol levels in their blood (called serum cholesterol) are prone to heart disease and stroke and since the fatty deposits associated with atherosclerosis have been found to contain large quantities of cholesterol, many scientists believed in the 1950s and early 1960s, as many believe today, that a reduction of cholesterol levels would be beneficial. Others, however, felt that atherosclerosis had a variety of causes. The Food and Drug Administration, in an official ruling published in the *Federal Register* on December 10, 1959, noted that the "role of cholesterol in heart and artery diseases has not been established" and that a "causal relationship between blood cholesterol levels and these diseases has not been proven." Nevertheless, the statistical association between cholesterol and atherosclerosis made cholesterol a chief target in the effort to prevent heart disease. Some authorities advocated dietary restrictions to keep cholesterol levels low. Others, aware that the body (principally in the liver) manufactures 70 to 80 percent of its cholesterol, have sought chemical means. Although many substances were being used with varying degrees of success, there was no effective and safe cholesterol-lowering agent of universal application. If one could be developed, the payoff in terms of both profit and prestige would be enormous.

In 1959 a Merrell employee estimated that some sixty million Americans over forty were potential customers for a drug which could ensure normal cholesterol levels. At around the same time the then director of Merrell's medical research department reported to the company's chief scientist as well as to its president that Dr. William Hollander, one of the clinical researchers working with MER/29, had "predicted a relatively large market" for the drug and that it "was his suggestion that a dose of one capsule daily would be indicated for all people over the age of thirty-five." Dr. Hollander was said to have "implied that in many respects it would be like vitamin therapy." The drug would be taken each day, every day for life. At nearly twenty cents a pill, the wholesale cost of one MER/29 capsule, the sales potential for such a product would be a staggering $4.25 billion a year, far greater than the *total* nationwide expenditure for pharmaceutial products in 1960. In comparison, in the late fifties and early sixties, when MER/29 was developed and marketed, Richardson-Merrell's average annual gross sales was only $120 million. Even if cholesterol-lowering therapy were limited to those patients with existing cardiovascular disease, estimated by a Merrell employee in late 1959 to number around five million, the potential annual gross sales for such a drug would be over $350 million, three times the total gross sales of Merrell's corporate parent. At the end of the cholesterol rainbow was a large pot of gold indeed. It awaited the company which could come up with the right product.

Merrell's attempt to develop an effective cholesterol-lowering agent focused on another of its products, the synthetic estrogen Tace. In the early 1950s it was observed that if the molecular structure of synthetic estrogenic hormones was chemically altered, the resulting substance might be able to block the body's synthesis of cholesterol. A young Merrell research chemist by the name of Frank Palopoli built on this knowledge and, after many years of hard work, succeeded in altering Tace's molecular structure in such ways that he thought some of the resulting compounds might be useful in combatting cholesterol. One of these, a chemical synthesised by Palopoli in 1956 and initially given the code name WSM 5052, was so effective in animals that Merrell scientists held their breath. Were they on the verge of a breakthrough? Would WSM 5052 lead them to the pot of gold? Much work remained, however, before their hopes for WSM 5052, later called MER/29, materialized.

Any new drug must pass a long and hazardous course from the research chemist's test tube to the pharmacist's shelf or physician's prescription pad. Many chemicals are developed in drug-company laboratories; few ever make it to the market. A drug must first be evaluated and tested in animals, and then, if it appears to be both safe and effective, it is tried out in humans. Finally, all the test data are gathered in a large, usually multivolume compendium of documents called a New Drug Application (NDA) and submitted to the Food and Drug Administration for its approval.

There are no drugs which are absolutely safe, that is, free from all side effects in all people. Thus, of necessity, the good must be weighed against the bad. Prior to the 1962 Kefauver-Harris amendments the FDA theoretically could not pass on a new drug's effectiveness, but only on its safety. In practice, however, many of the FDA medical officers evaluated the new drug as a whole, balancing its relative efficacy against its relative safety. Only if the latter were significantly outweighed by the former would the NDA be formally approved or "made effective."

The decision to approve a new drug for sale is always exceedingly difficult. Huge quantities of scientific data must be examined and evaluated. This enormous task is compounded by the fact that all the information the FDA receives on a drug is supplied by the drug company. The FDA does not independently test new drugs. Drug companies are profit-making organizations and they lobby extensively if it appears that the FDA medical officer to whom their NDA was assigned for evaluation has the slightest doubt as to the drug's worth. Pressure on a medical officer, sometimes a young doctor just out of internship, is often so great that dispassionate evaluation of an NDA is sometimes impossible. Torn betwen nagging doubts as to a drug's worth or safety and the incessant badgering by the drug company's representatives, and perhaps by his own superiors as well, to reach a decision, the medical officer will sometimes release a drug about which he has serious reservations. The medical officer who approved MER/29's NDA would later tell a reporter that he "released the drug with the knowledge that things might appear later which were not obvious at the time." Unfortunately, his misgivings would prove justified. Only by then it was too late for those who were already injured.

The New Drug Application for MER/29 was filed on July 24, 1959, some three years after it first appeared in Palopoli's test tubes. During those three years it had been tested on animals in Merrell's laboratories and in humans at various clinics and hospitals. The NDA purported to include "full reports of all investigations that have been made to show whether or not the drug is safe for use." The application originally consisted of 285 pages, 60 of which described the animal work. The clinical investigations, as the human trials are called, on 116 patients at seven medical centers were reported on in 174 pages. The remaining 51 pages described MER/29's chemical composition, its method of manufacture, and the description of its proposed packaging and labeling.

On April 19, 1960, despite strong misgivings by some FDA staff members, the NDA was made effective and MER/29 was approved for general sale as a prescription drug. Shortly thereafter, an extensive advertising campaign was launched; MER/29, described as a new breakthrough in medical research, was announced as "the first safe agent to inhibit body-produced cholesterol."

While not all members of the medical profession responded as enthusiastically as Merrell might have hoped, MER/29 proved to be a very popular and profitable drug. A poll of

Current clinical research has
established that approximately 3/4 of total cholesterol
is produced within the body: thus the therapeutic approach
should focus on control of cholesterol biosynthesis.

Introducing

MER/29

(brand of triparanol)

...the first safe agent to inhibit
body-produced cholesterol

...the first to lower excess
cholesterol levels in both tissue
and serum, irrespective of diet

DOSAGE: One 250 mg. capsule daily, before breakfast.

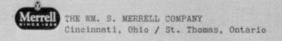 THE WM. S. MERRELL COMPANY
Cincinnati, Ohio / St. Thomas, Ontario

Trademark: 'MER/29'

The first page of a two-page advertisement which appeared in
fifteen major medical journals in June, July, and August 1960.

physicians conducted by *Medical Research Digest* named it the most significant advance in medical therapy for 1960, its very first year, and Richardson-Merrell's 1961 Annual Report boasted proudly that MER/29 was the nation's "leading anti-cholesterol drug" and that it was the company's "largest selling" prescription product.

All, however, was not sweetness and light. There were disturbing reports of serious side effects associated with MER/29 therapy. Some patients developed a severe and often painful scaly skin condition known as ichthyosis ("fishlike" skin) and began to lose their hair. Ominously, a few patients developed cataracts, an irreversible clouding of the lens of the eye. While the skin condition would clear and hair would regrow after MER/29 was discontinued, cataract-caused blindness could be alleviated only by surgically removing the now opaque lenses. Following surgery the patient would have to wear thick eyeglasses or special contact lenses in order to see at all.

Disturbed by the increasing evidence that MER/29 was toxic, many in the FDA wanted Merrell to withdraw the drug. Consideration was also given to suspending the effectiveness of the NDA, thereby prohibiting its further sale. But Merrell remained obdurate, and strongly resisted any attempt to have the drug removed from the market. Then the carefully constructed house of cards collapsed.

One evening in late February 1962 Thomas Rice, a local Cincinnati inspector for the FDA, was riding home from work. Carson Jordan, the husband of a former employee in Merrell's toxicology-pathology laboratory and a member of Rice's car pool, mentioned that his wife had once been directed to falsify a chart in connection with MER/29. Rice later checked the story with Jordan's wife, Beulah, and informed Washington. On Monday morning April 9, 1962, after several weeks of unexplained delay, Rice, Dr. John Nestor, the medical officer who was then in charge of the MER/29 file, and Dr. Edwin Goldenthal, an FDA pharmacologist, paid a surprise visit to the Merrell laboratories armed with a certificate of inspection. During an investigation lasting two days they found substantial evidence that scientific data submitted to the FDA had been falsified. On April 12, 1962, two years after MER/29 had been approved for sale, Merrell informed the FDA that it was removing MER/29 from the market. In a speech given four months later to an American Bar Association group, Deputy Food and Drug Commissioner John L. Harvey admitted that "in retrospect, it is apparent that the drug should not have gone on the market in the first place."

3

"I Do Not Wish to Contend"

"They have drive, they have hopes, and they have visions. This drug was one of them." *

On December 20, 1963, a special federal grand jury sitting in Washington, D.C., issued a detailed twelve-count indictment charging that the Wm. S. Merrell Co. together with its parent company Richardson-Merrell and three of its employees falsified scientific data submitted to the Food and Drug Administration in connection with MER/29. The individuals named in the indictment were Merrell's chief scientist and director of research, Harold W. Werner; its director of biological sciences, Evert Florus Van Maanen; and the chief of its toxicology-pathology laboratory, William M. King. Originally, the companies and the three scientists entered pleas of not guilty to the indictment, but on March 24, 1964, these were changed to *nolo contendere* ("I do not wish to contend") in exchange for the dismissal of some of the counts. Although United States district court judge Matthew M. McGuire, who accepted the changed pleas, made it clear that these were tantamount to pleas of guilty, the *nolo contendere* response to the indictment effectively precluded use of the criminal charges in the numerous civil suits brought against the companies by persons alleging that they had been injured by MER/29. The companies were fined a total of

* Summation of former Deputy Attorney General and former United States district court judge Lawrence E. Walsh defending the actions of the officers of Richardson-Merrell in *Roginsky* v. *Richardson-Merrell,* March 7, 1966.

23

$80,000, and the individual defendants were each sentenced to six months' probation.

Harold W. Werner was a Merrell vice-president as well as the company's director of research and chief scientist. It was his responsibility to coordinate all the scientific departments with one another and to advise the company's top management, none of whom had any scientific training. The fact that Merrell's sole business was the development, evaluation, and marketing of new drugs made Werner's position exceedingly important. He was the eyes and ears of a management both deaf and blind with respect to the highly specialized area of their company's business.* As events later proved, Dr. Werner was himself in need of a good pair of eyeglasses and a hearing aid.

Of the four departments reporting directly to Dr. Werner perhaps the most important in the early stages of a drug's development was the biological sciences department, headed by Evert Florus Van Maanen. Van Maanen came to this country shortly after the end of World War II, having first received his Ph.D. in pharmacy in his native Netherlands and having, so he testified later, worked closely with the Dutch underground in opposition to the Nazis. In 1949 he received another Ph.D., this time in medical sciences, from Harvard.

Dr. Van Maanen became director of Merrell's biological sciences department in 1955, and all drug research in animals was done in the laboratories under his jurisdiction. These laboratories would analyze the action of newly synthesized compounds to determine if they could possibly be beneficial

---

* Merrell's president, Frank N. Getman, testified that he never read any part of the New Drug Application for MER/29. He also explained that since he did not understand scientific papers, he would either scan them or read a summary. Insofar as departmental reports were concerned, Getman testified that sometimes he would not even look at them. "A lot of these reports went over my desk and I didn't open the cover, the volume. At other times, I opened it to get an impression of the fields in which we were working in these departments."

to man. If a compound was found to be promising (as, for example, WSM 5052 was found to lower cholesterol levels in the test animals), it would then be evaluated for safety in another laboratory under Dr. Van Maanen's jurisdiction: toxicology-pathology. In a sense, toxicology-pathology had the most important task of any of Merrell's laboratories; for a drug is useful only if it is safe, and it was toxicology-pathology's job to investigate whether a compound shown to be promising in the other laboratories was sufficiently free from adverse side effects in animals to warrant its further testing in humans. Toxicology-pathology was not only the last testing station before experimentation in humans, but even after a new drug had been given to people in the clinical trials, the results of the animal tests remained important in studying areas of continued concern.

William M. King became the head of Merrell's toxicology-pathology laboratory in September 1958, when he was thirty-three years old. He had no prior experience in the drug industry and had just completed his graduate work in pharmacology and toxicology at the University of Minnesota. He had not yet obtained his Ph.D. degree (the department directors and the other laboratory heads were all either Ph.D.s or M.D.s). This fact—discovered by Merrell's president, Frank N. Getman, in December 1961, when MER/29 was already in trouble—was to haunt the company throughout the later investigations, for not only was King constantly referred to as "Dr." King in all internal company memoranda but he was also represented as a Ph.D. to the medical profession and to the FDA. King eventually completed his Ph.D. requirements after he left Merrell in June 1962.

The young researcher's responsibility as head of toxicology-pathology was increased considerably by Merrell's apparent policy of permitting its scientists to report the results of their investigations without reference to any observations they thought to be insignificant or unreliable. As unique as this policy might seem to those of us who have been taught from childhood that the glory of the scientific method is that *all* observations are reported and analyzed, Merrell's major defense during the subsequent investigations and trials was that its scientists could use their own best judgment in deciding which of their findings to report and which to forget. Dr. Van Maanen testified that the observations would be released only if "the results warranted a report" based on a prior determination of their "reliability and significance."

Dr. Robert H. McMaster, who as an associate director of Merrell's medical research department was directly responsible for coordinating the testing of MER/29 in humans, evidently also believed that not everything seen in the laboratory had to be revealed. At one of the trials he was asked what Merrell's practice was with respect to the reporting of scientific facts. He replied: "The practice was that such facts ought to be disclosed to all such persons who had a right to know them, but that this included only those facts that were significant or that had some bearing on whether or not the drug should be prescribed for people's use." Thus, Richardson-Merrell's president, H. Robert Marschalk, explaining Merrell's conduct to the company's stockholders in a letter dated March 24, 1964, wrote that company scientists "could properly exercise professional judgment in determining which test reports and results were sufficiently significant and material to require reporting to the FDA."

Despite Merrell's defensive stance that their scientists had a right to screen their observations and report only those they thought were significant, the company must have realized that scientific data has to be not only accurate, but complete as well. In a memorandum dated April 24, 1962, directed to Merrell's president, Frank N. Getman, Van Maanen (who himself was accused of directing the falsification of data) explained that insofar as King was responsible for the discrepancies between the reports submitted to the FDA and their own laboratory records, he was certain that they were inadvertent, caused by King's "lack of appreciation for details." This *post facto* apologia was supported by Van Maanen's earlier evaluations of King's employment record. In July 1959, after ten months on the job, Van Maanen reported that while King was an "excellent histopathologist and uses his knowledge very well toward product development" he was "sometimes too much swayed by his own convictions" and that he "needs guidance in reporting on complex studies." A year later, King's performance evaluation sheet noted that his research work "lacks accuracy." This criticism was repeated in August 1961, when King's written reports were said to be incomplete and to "often lack detailed analysis of important facts." The 1961 evaluation sheet also charged that King, in his oral presentations was "not always sticking to facts" and "often inclined to sidestep problems." Employment evaluation sheets for Dr. Van Maanen during the period 1959 to 1961, on the other hand, complained that he had "an excessively strong desire to always win," and that sometimes his "personal preference interferes with his judgment."

Although King's arrival at Merrell in September 1958 had marked the turning point in the development of MER/29 (much of the falsified data originated in his laboratory), he was never called by either side to testify in any of the civil actions. He thus remains somewhat of an enigma—an elusive shadow, discussed but never seen, damned but never heard.

Immediately following the surprise FDA inspection and the withdrawal of MER/29 from the market, both King and Van Maanen were suspended with pay while Merrell conducted its own investigation into what had gone wrong. In June 1962 they were both asked to resign. Van Maanen returned to a full-time position as associate professor of pharmacology at the University of Cincinnati College of Medicine. King reportedly also returned to teaching.

The indictment of Werner, Van Maanen, and King, and

the dismissal of the latter two, does not bleach blameless the rest of the company. The common thread throughout the entire MER/29 story is that people entrusted with developing and marketing medicines for human use either deliberately or through carelessness breached that solemn trust. That is the true tragedy of MER/29: the responsibility for which Merrell did "not wish to contend."

4

Monkey Business

"As you may know, we have recently obtained evidence that the Wm. S. Merrell Co. falsified data submitted as part of the New Drug Application for MER/29. In view of this we cannot consider the information submitted by this firm as reliable without thorough verification." *

During the period MER/29 was developed and tested, the toxicology-pathology laboratory at Merrell employed approximately thirteen persons, most of whom were technicians without any formal scientific background. They did the bulk of the work, caring for the animals, weighing and dosing them, and making general observations as to their conditions. The actual autopsy work and analysis was performed by someone with scientific training. Until William M. King became the head of the laboratory, in September 1958, this work was performed mainly by James Knox Smith. He was the leader of the toxicology group in what had been the endocrinology-toxicology-pathology laboratory, headed by Charles Thompson. When Thompson left in early 1958 Smith became the laboratory's unofficial chief. Later, when King joined Merrell in September, the endocrinology section was separated from toxicology-pathology and became the fifth laboratory under Van Maanen's jurisdiction.

King's arrival on the scene was greeted with little en-

* Directive dated May 7, 1962, from Dr. William H. Kessenich, chief of the Division of New Drugs of the Food and Drug Administration, to members of his staff.

thusiasm in the laboratory he was to head. Everyone liked
and respected Smith, so they were naturally disappointed that
he had not been promoted and they resented their new boss.
According to Bruce Umberger, then a technician in the laboratory, the most resentful was Beulah Jordan. She complained
to Umberger that King was "acting like a big shot because
he had just started with the company and they were allowing
him to buy things [which apparently Smith was not allowed
to do]." She noted, however, that "soon he would be put in
his place."

Mrs. Jordan's dislike for King was evident in her later
testimony. She related that when he first arrived he made it
clear that he wished to be "referred to as 'Dr. King' and
pointed to a small diploma hanging on the wall of his office."
He allegedly also told them that they were "not to associate
with people in other labs during lunch." One of her more
serious charges was that King drank heavily. "There were
times," she recalled, "when Mr. King came in after lunch and
he had so much to drink that he could not do his job properly
and he would go into his office and close the door. Although
we received instructions from Mr. King that he and he alone
would do the autopsy work, because of his drinking problem,
we would take over his job, so that the time schedule required
would be maintained. After Mr. Smith left, the situation became more acute, since we did not have Mr. Smith, who
could take over most of the problems that arose and we did
not have his competent guidance."

King would also make her go home "to fix a shaker of
martinis" for him to drink "during working hours," Mrs. Jordan testified. On one occasion, she alleged, King's insistence
that his subordinates "join him in an evening of drinking"
spoiled a planned gathering of friends at her house. "Two
days before the event, Mr. King decided to have a cocktail
party at his home, and he threatened all the employees that
if they did not attend his cocktail party they need not report

to work Monday." She said that both she and her husband were thus forced to leave their guests, who were going on to a dinner dance, and attend King's party.

As already noted, King was never called to testify. However, Bruce Umberger stated that he had never seen King drunk and charged that Beulah Jordan was the main cause of any problems. "As far as I was concerned," Umberger testified, "she thrived on turmoil in the laboratory. If something was going wrong, she was bound to be in the center of it. As long as she personally didn't get hurt by it, she just thrived on it." Dr. Van Maanen similarly testified that King had complained to him that Mrs. Jordan "was not cooperating" with her co-workers and "was spreading certain rumors" about them. Specifically, she had allegedly refused to work with another technician and had accused one man of making a pass at her. She also allegedly complained that the company physician was "too free with his hands."

The dissension in the laboratory came to a head at the company picnic on Saturday June 13, 1959, when, according to Bruce Umberger, Beulah Jordan, who "had possibly a little too much to drink," went over to the head of the pharmacology laboratory (similarly under Van Maanen's jurisdiction) and complained about working for King. A number of her co-workers overheard, and on Monday morning they reported her comments to King. "Sometime after that," testified Umberger, "he called her in, and they had a discussion, I guess in the office. Later on, she came out and slammed the door and went out through the lab into a back area, like a storage area. It's outside the building. She was there for some time. Dr. King came through and asked where she was. He was told where she was, and he went out there and talked to her. Later, she came back in and slammed the door, and she said that the company wasn't big enough for both of them, and she left."

That Monday was Mrs. Jordan's last day on the job, and

her version of the events culminating in the exit cliché of grade B westerns is substantially the same as Umberger's. At the picnic, she later testified, she told the head of the pharmacology laboratory that she "didn't like what was going on in toxicology" and "would like to get into another department." She asked him if she could transfer to his laboratory, but "apparently he told Dr. King what I said and King wasn't too happy about it, so when I went back to work on Monday we had quite a discussion. I told him that I didn't approve of some of the things that went on in toxicology; that I didn't want to be in that department. One word led to another and I quit."

Mrs. Jordan then told the personnel director that she "had no intention of staying on with Mr. King." She also stated that she would not "stand for being required to change lab data" and "gave them a written reason for my leaving, which was that I would not be a part of the changing of lab data as required by Mr. King and Dr. Van Maanen." If this latter reason was ever communicated to Merrell's personnel director as Mrs. Jordan claims, nothing further was heard of her charge until nearly two years later when her husband repeated it in that fateful car-pool ride home. Her alleged "written reason" for leaving was never located in any of the subsequent investigations into MER/29.

The King-Jordan tempest, which flared in the middle of June 1959, is significant for two reasons. The first is that it shattered a cherished myth. Drug-company laboratories are represented, to the lay and professional public alike, as being paradigms of scientific discipline, of professionalism and humanitarian concern. And so they should be. For the simple truth is that drug companies exist for one reason, to make drugs intended to save human lives or alleviate human misery. It is a high calling indeed. What may be well tolerated in a shoe factory is intolerable in a drug-company laboratory. If the backbiting, petty tyranny, and divided loyalties revealed by the Umberger, Jordan, and Van Maanen testimony existed in the Merrell toxicology-pathology laboratory and if Mrs. Jordan's allegations of King's frequent alcoholic incapacitations are true, the company's management was as shockingly remiss in this area as they were in connection with King's nonexistent Ph.D. That management seemed so blissfully unaware of what was going on beneath them is not an excuse, as some have claimed, but an indictment.

The second reason that the King-Jordan tempest is significant is, of course, that it was Beulah Jordan, or more accurately her husband, who blew the whistle on Merrell's falsification of data. Her charges concerned a sixteen-month toxicity study in monkeys.

Starting in late 1957, several monkeys were given MER/29 by mouth each day, five days a week. Other monkeys acted as controls and were given placebos (sugar pills). Both groups of monkeys were treated the same and were fed from the same formula. Each monkey was numbered and each Friday it would be weighed. It was Beulah Jordan's task to enter the weights in a laboratory notebook.

The weights of the animals were important for two reasons. First, the animals on MER/29 would receive a certain predetermined number of milligrams of the drug for every kilogram of body weight.° Thus the dose an animal received during the week was determined by his weight on the preceding Friday. Second, any unusual gain or loss in weight might indicate that the drug was having an adverse effect.

In May 1959, when the study was completed, Beulah Jordan compiled and graphed the average monthly weights for each of the monkeys. The graph, which was to be submitted to the Food and Drug Administration in support of the MER/29 NDA, reflected among other things that monkey 49, a female drugged monkey which had become the laboratory's "pet" (she was referred to as "Old forty-niner"), had

° While the weights would be recorded in kilograms (a kilogram equals approximately 2.2 pounds), Merrell evidently was unable to obtain a metric scale because the animals were weighed in pounds and the technicians had to use a conversion chart taped to the inside of their record books.

lost 2.4 kilograms during the final month and that two other monkeys were sacrificed several weeks earlier than the others.

This was apparently unacceptable, for, as Mrs. Jordan later testified, King told her to take the graph to Dr. Van Maanen and he directed her to make certain changes. He initially asked her to extend the weight lines of the two monkeys which had been sacrificed first so that they would be even with the weight of the others. After this was done, he instructed her to eliminate the sharp decline in monkey 49's weight line. "He said he didn't like the point of this monkey dropping like this," she recalled, and directed her to bring the line "more on an even keel." He also told her to include the monthly weights of an additional monkey in the revised graph. He specified that that it was to be added as a control even though it had been given *another* drug (one similar to MER/29) as part of a *different* experiment.

Mrs. Jordan said that when she informed King what Van Maanen had directed, he replied that "Dr. Van Maanen was higher up and that I should do it as I was told and to keep quiet"; which she did. Nothing further was heard about the monkey graph until Mrs. Jordan's husband related the incident to FDA inspector Thomas Rice. Dr. Van Maanen would later deny her charges and attempt to explain the discrepancies as being caused by the "lack of appreciation for details on the part of Bill King." He admitted, however, that he could not "understand why I did not detect these mistakes."

As noted earlier, Rice reported Mrs. Jordan's charges to Washington. On Sunday April 8, 1962, Dr. John O. Nestor, the FDA medical officer who was then overseeing MER/29, and Dr. Edwin Goldenthal, an FDA pharmacologist, flew out to Cincinnati. On Monday morning they and inspector Rice appeared at Merrell's gate unannounced. They presented their certificate of inspection to Fred Lamb, Merrell's house counsel, and spent most of the morning reviewing reports concerning the possibility that MER/29 was causing cataracts. After lunch they went to King's laboratory. With them were Dr. Van Maanen and Dr. F. Joseph Murray (Ph.D.), who as director of the scientific relations department was the company's liaison officer with the Food and Drug Administration. They reviewed the animal data and specifically the monkey records. As Dr. Nestor later explained, the FDA "had received some information that raised questions about the validity of some of the data that had been sent to us pertaining to monkeys." This "some information" was of course Rice's report on what Beulah Jordan had told him.

Nestor and his colleagues found numerous instances where data submitted to the FDA did not coincide with Merrell's laboratory records. These discrepancies were brought to Merrell's attention before they left Monday afternoon. On Monday night the FDA group reviewed their notes, and when they returned on Tuesday morning, as Nestor later testified, they outlined "for the representatives of the firm the questions that had been raised or the discrepancies that we wanted explained." Merrell was unable to explain but said "that they would work it out and do the best they could." Nestor and Dr. Goldenthal then returned to Washington.

Merrell's view of Nestor's surprise visit is contained in a confidential memorandum dated April 11, 1962, from Dr. Murray to eight members of Merrell's corporate hierarchy, including president Getman, as well as Richardson-Merrell's general counsel. The first page of the memorandum concerns the FDA group's apparent desire to review the recent cataract reports and only on the second page does Dr. Murray mention that "Dr. Goldenthal expressed interest in reviewing some of the animal data" and that this interest "appeared to be confined to monkeys." Then, in the middle of page two, he lets the shoe fall. "In reviewing our records on the monkeys, a number of discrepancies were noted from data submitted in the original NDA. These discrepancies were as follows:

1) A rapid loss of weight amounting to 5.3 pounds took place in one month in monkey #49, as noted in raw data curves. Curves submitted to F.D.A. did not reflect this weight loss.
2) Autopsy records for monkey #34 could not be located in any research book.
3) There was a conflict of dates recorded for autopsies for monkeys #34, 49, and 51, with as many as three different dates recorded for an autopsy.
4) Records differed as to whether monkey 51 had been dosed for 8 months before autopsy.
5) There was a discrepancy in sequential numbering of animal autopsies.
6) There was a possible conflict on dose records in at least one animal.

When the FDA group returned Tuesday morning and asked for explanations, Dr. Murray continued, they "were advised that we had not had sufficient time since their departure to go through all records but that we were working on it. Dr. Goldenthal asked whether he could review data of feeding experiments in monkeys with the hopes of finding some explanation for the weight loss in monkey #49. No records of this type could be found." Murray then related why Dr. Nestor considered the discrepancies to be serious. "He stated that the F.D.A. pharmacology group had some real reservations on the toxicity of MER/29 in rats and dogs. However, Merrell had argued that the monkeys showed no toxicity, and this was a strong factor in getting the NDA approved." In conclusion, Dr. Murray noted that "Dr. Nestor reiterated his personal convictions that MER/29 is too toxic to justify remaining on the market."

One day after this memorandum was written, Merrell notified the FDA that it was "voluntarily" withdrawing the drug.

Whether the monkey data was deliberately changed, as was charged by Mrs. Jordan, or whether the errors were the result of sloppy work, as alleged by Van Maanen, the Food and Drug Administration was admittedly supplied with false information—not only with respect to the sixteen-month monkey experiment but in connection with other animal studies as well.

One of these was a 1957 rat experiment. The animals were divided into three groups of sixteen (eight males and and eight females). One group of rats received 37.5 mg. of MER/29 per kilogram of body weight, five days a week. The rats in the second group were given a daily dose of 75 mg. of the drug, and the third group served as the controls. The experiment lasted six weeks, at the end of which time the surviving animals were weighed, sacrificed, and autopsied. The autopsy procedure involved weighing the rats' organs and analyzing their blood. The female rats receiving 75 mg. of MER/29, however, tolerated the drug badly, and seven died before the end of the six weeks. Since the usual autopsy procedure is performed only on those animals which are deliberately sacrificed (and not on those which die from the drug), the organs of these animals were not weighed and their blood was not analyzed. Nor was this done for the eighth female high-dose rat, which had been sacrificed one week early.

When Merrell reported the results of this six-week rat experiment to the FDA, the company not only stated that merely four of the eight female rats receiving 75 mg. of MER/29 had died but gave organ weights and blood values for all eight rats even though none had been obtained. The figures were lifted from a different experiment, a three-month rat study. In this three-month experiment the rats received either 25 or 50 mg. of MER/29, and here too the high-dose females were very badly affected. Accordingly, they were sacrificed at the end of six weeks rather than twelve, at which time their organs were weighed and their blood was analyzed. King, or whoever in toxicology-pathology under his supervision, in preparing the organ-weight and blood-value tables for the 75 mg. female rats (which are found on pages 39-41 of the

NDA) copied them from the tables for the 50 mg. female rats (found on pages 48 and 50 of the NDA). These are reproduced in Table 1.

In one of the later trials, former Judge Walsh discounted an evil motive in this instance, noting that "you can't be this stupid intentionally."

There were other discrepancies between what Merrell observed and what Merrell disclosed. In June 1958, some three months before King joined Merrell, the company had prepared a brochure so that potential clinical investigators could evaluate the MER/29 animal investigations. The brochure noted that structural changes had been observed in the lymphocytes (white blood cells) of a monkey and rats on MER/29 and termed these altered lymphocytes "bizarre." It was further reported that rats given MER/29 had a higher percentage of reticulocytes (young or immature red blood cells) in their blood than did the control rats. As the late heart specialist Dr. Lawrence Kinsell testified, the higher-than-normal incidence of reticulocytes could be an indication that the bone marrow (which manufactures red blood cells) was being whipped up by the drug and that the condition could lead to bone-marrow exhaustion.

In a memorandum dated May 5, 1959, Dr. Van Maanen requested Dr. King "to delete all material on the funny lymphocytes" from the brochure's second edition and questioned "whether the reticulocyte change in the rat experiment needs the emphasis it has." Accordingly, when King prepared the new edition he omitted all reference to any of the blood changes. They were similarly not reported to the FDA. Dr. Van Maanen later explained this by noting that King, in consultation with an expert in Minnesota (whom King had described as a "close associate and friend of many years" as well as a "top notch" animal-blood specialist), had concluded that blood changes were "most likely" caused by an infection and were not related to MER/29. The blood changes being neither significant nor reliable, Van Maanen and King felt they did not have to be reported.

Table 1

The following are blood-value figures for the 75 mg. female rats and the 50 mg. female rats found in the NDA:

	Hemoglobin Gms. Percent Initial—Final		Hematocrit % Packed Cells Initial—Final		Leucocytes Thousands/mm³ Initial—Final		Granulocytes Percent Initial—Final	
75 mg., page 41 of the NDA	12.5	13.3	45	44	14.7	24.7	20	25
50 mg., page 48 of the NDA	12.5	13.3	44.9	44.4	14.72	24.73	20	25

The following are weight values for the 75 mg. female rats and the 50 mg. female rats found in the NDA:

	Body weight gm.	Heart gm.	Spleen gm.	Liver gm.	L. Kidney gm.	R. Kidney gm.	L. Adrenal mg.	R. Adrenal mg.	Ovaries mg.	Uterus mg.	Thyroid mg.
Average absolute wts.											
75 mg., page 39 of the NDA	139	0.61	1.05	6.3	0.62	0.67	30.2	28.0	24.5	79.7	(blank)
50 mg., page 50 of the NDA	139	0.61	1.05	6.3	0.62	0.67	30.2	28.0	24.5	79.7	(blank)
Average relative wts. mg/gm											
75 mg., page 40 of the NDA	139	4.42	7.70	45.98	4.48	4.82	.227	.210	.18	.58	(blank)
50 mg., page 50 of the NDA	139	4.42	7.70	45.98	4.48	4.82	.227	.210	.18	.58	(blank)

They had been reported in the first brochure, however, and this prompted one outside researcher, Dr. Jane Desforges, to ask Merrell's medical research department to send her blood smears so that she could study the changes herself. Medical research passed the request on to Dr. Van Maanen. He refused. In a memorandum dated October 6, 1958, Van Maanen noted that he had discussed the request with Werner and King and that "all three of us concur in the opinion that at the moment it would not be in the interest of the company and our product to send such a smear to interested clinical hematologists." He explained that they were still studying the implications of the blood changes and that they believed that "clinical hematologists may not be experienced enough with changes observed in animal hematology and that their misinterpretation of our results might do premature harm to a potentially good compound."

The next day the director of medical research wrote to Dr. Werner complaining that the "decision not to release blood smears from our toxicological studies to our hematological consultant, Dr. Jane Desforges, represents a serious handicap in the MER/29 studies. As you know, Dr. McMaster and I have a moral and medical obligation to use MER/29 safely. Accordingly, we are both anxious to find out more about the blood changes which have been reported in experimental animals." There is no indication of whether the smears were ever released.

These studies were not only misrepresented to the Food and Drug Administration, but as seen from the deletion of all references to the "bizarre" and "funny" lymphocytes and the abnormally high incidence of reticulocytes in the second brochure, they were misrepresented to the medical profession as well.

Another misrepresentation of Merrell's observations took place at the so-called Princeton Conference.

In December 1959 Merrell, as part of its pre-marketing promotional effort, sponsored a two-day symposium on MER/29,
and while it took place at the Princeton Inn in Princeton,
New Jersey, it was not connected with Princeton University.
Merrell invited various well-known specialists and scientists
who either were interested in MER/29 as an agent to lower
cholesterol levels or who had done some work with the then
experimental drug. In the course of the conference many
scientific papers were presented, and the researchers were
subjected to questions.* One of those who presented a paper
was William M. King, identified as a Ph.D. and the head of
toxicology and pathology at Merrell. King's paper, entitled
"The Toxicology of MER/29," concluded that MER/29 was
a safe drug based in part on the fact that long-term administration of "relatively high doses" of MER/29 to monkeys
"did not affect the body weight" and that no "untoward
hematopoietic [related to the formation of blood cells] response
has been demonstrated in the rat, dog or monkey."

King's report was replete with errors. Aside from ignoring
monkey 49's weight loss and the blood changes, King gave
inaccurate dosages and duration of treatment for the various
monkeys. For example, in one table setting forth the observed
blood values for the MER/29-treated monkeys he correctly
identified monkey 25 as receiving the drug for only seven
months but incorrectly stated that it received 40 mg. for the
entire time. In another table, this one detailing the results
of certain liver-function tests—which were of special importance because most of the body's cholesterol is made in the
liver, and a drug which interferes with the liver's synthesis
of cholesterol might also be expected to interfere with some
of its other functions—monkey 25 is represented as having

* In May 1960 the conference proceedings were reprinted as a special
issue of the professional journal *Progress in Cardiovascular Diseases*. It runs
for approximately 180 pages. Merrell sent a summary of these proceedings to
over 100,000 physicians.

been on the drug for the full sixteen months, and this time at 20 mg.! °

Admittedly this error could have been caused by hasty preparation of the chart. However, monkey 25 was autopsied in March 1958, some six months before King was hired, and the man who was then the acting head of toxicology-pathology testified that he did not perform any liver-function tests on monkey 25 (these have to be done while the animal is alive), nor did he recall anyone performing liver-function tests on that monkey. One of King's conclusions was that MER/29 "does not alter measurable liver function in the monkey."

Although Werner, Van Maanen, King, and the Merrell Company were indicted for falsely reporting the results of the monkey and rat experiments, it is difficult to appraise the true significance of the discrepancies. Hindsight is generally either a magnifier or a reducer, transforming the importance of past events in light of present knowledge. Certainly, when Merrell's failure to disclose the blood changes and some of the other observations is viewed in this light their significance seems to shrink. MER/29 caused hair loss, fishlike skin, and cataracts. There were few, if any, cases of blood damage in humans. However, the true significance of the discrepancies can only be evaluated by examining whether, had Merrell made a full disclosure of their observations, the drug would have been subjected to further scrutiny, thereby increasing the possibility that its true toxic effects in humans would have emerged.

On September 14, 1959, some two months after the New Drug Application was filed, Dr. Jerome Epstein, the medical officer to whom MER/29 was then assigned, wrote Merrell and requested that additional long-term animal experiments be run, since "the drug is by nature one which will receive chronic [long term] use" and as the "data you have sub-

---

° The monkey actually received 40 mg. of MER/29 for four months, 20 mg. for two months, and 10 mg. for three weeks.

mitted [in the NDA] suggests a low margin of safety." On September 24 Dr. Murray replied that Merrell was "somewhat surprised by the statement that our data 'suggest a low margin of safety,'" protesting that they felt their findings "had demonstrated a reasonably high margin of safety." He then summarized the animal data which had been submitted, noting among other things that "body weight gains were not affected [*sic.*] in rats or monkeys" at high doses and that there was "no untoward hematopoietic response" in the rats or monkeys. He concluded by emphasizing that Merrell strongly felt "that the 16-month study of monkeys has more than adequately demonstrated the safety of MER/29."

In another letter, this one dated October 13, 1959, to Dr. Epstein, Dr. Murray reiterated that "the significance of the studies carried out in the monkey has been entirely overlooked." He pointed out that they "submitted data on three monkeys dosed continuously for 16 months.* If a new drug fails to show untoward effects in three animals, such effects would probably show up only in unreasonably large groups of twenty-five or more. Such groups are impractical and not used generally." The unspoken premise of this latter sentence was that the drug should be released for widespread use in humans without putting the company to the additional expense and burden of thoroughly proving its safety by rigorously testing it on large animal colonies.

In any event, while the FDA did require additional animal testing before approving MER/29 for general prescription sale (as we shall shortly see), Dr. Nestor indicated to Dr. Murray at the time of the FDA's surprise visit that Merrell's argument "that the monkeys showed no toxicity . . . was a strong factor in getting the NDA approved." What would have happened had the FDA been given the full facts with

---

* This was not true. Monkey 51 was added to the sixteen-month experiment halfway through and thus was only dosed for eight months. Monkey 25 was autopsied at the end of seven months. The remaining two monkeys, 34 and 49, were dosed from September 1957 to February 1959, but were both off the drug for three weeks during March and April 1958.

respect to the monkey and rat experiments can only, of course, be a subject of speculation. Most likely they would have required additional evidence of MER/29's safety before releasing the drug for sale.

Nevertheless, the sixteen-month monkey experiment proved highly significant regardless of its scientific importance. If the FDA had not learned about monkey 49's weight loss and Merrell's apparent decision to squash the bug, it may never have uncovered the great mass of what Dr. Kessenich termed "falsified data submitted as part of the New Drug Application for MER/29." Monkey 49 was thus in a sense the catalyst plunged into a supersaturated solution: the discovery of the altered graph caused immediate crystallization of what had been a fluid situation. After that Merrell no longer defended its drug, and two days later told the FDA that it would be withdrawn. It is no wonder, therefore, that during the period when MER/29 was still an object of current controversy, Merrell's lawyers kept a straw monkey, the kind sold in Mexico as souvenirs, perched on one of the office cabinets. Around its neck hung the number "49."

While the discrepancies in the data submitted to the FDA in 1959 were not directly pertinent to MER/29's ability to cause cataracts, the discrepancies in the animal data submitted to FDA in 1960 were. As we have seen, the FDA wanted Merrell to run additional animal tests in the fall of 1959 because it felt the material already submitted indicated that the drug had a "low margin of safety." Merrell did not agree, and argued that the drug should be immediately released for sale. They noted that "we can ill afford to be wrong in our judgment on the introduction of any new product, and we do not feel that MER/29 is going to spoil our record." Inasmuch as other animal studies were already under way, Merrell promised to keep the FDA informed of their progress and expressed a willingness "to withdraw the product from the market if real toxicity problems were uncovered." The FDA declined this unique and somewhat startling promise to close the barn door if and when the horse escaped, and a meeting was arranged for October 16, 1959, to work things out. At that meeting, Merrell agreed to complete the tests currently under way, and to run a six-month study in dogs and a twelve-month rat study.

On February 18, 1960, Merrell forwarded a forty-two-page summary of the additional animal work for inclusion in their New Drug Application. The summary reported that eight out of twenty rats receiving 40 mg. of MER/29 developed an "opacity of the cornea" and conjunctivitis. It noted, however, that the corneal changes were "inflammatory" and "were not considered associated with drug therapy." There was no mention whether these "corneal opacities" were observed in the control animals. This was the first indication that MER/29 might be affecting the eye.

The eye is a tiny marvel of divine engineering. It discerns a comparatively narrow band of radiation, which we call "light," and thus enables us to "see" objects in its reflected glow. The part of the eye which senses light is the retina. An outgrowth of the brain, to which it is connected by the optic nerve, the retina can be likened to the film in a camera. The lens stands suspended toward the front of the eye and focuses light passing through it onto the retina. The intensity of light reaching the retina is controlled by the iris, which lies directly in front of the lens. The iris corresponds to the diaphragm of a camera; it narrows and enlarges its opening automatically in response to the light intensity. Directly in front of the lens and iris is a tiny chamber filled with a watery fluid known as the aqueous humor. The front side of this chamber is bounded by the cornea, a transparent portion of the eye's outer covering sometimes referred to as the "window" to the eye. It corresponds to the clear glass filter which a photographer places in front of his camera's lens to protect it from dirt and water. The conjunctiva is the tender membrane which lines the underside of the eyelids and extends as a thin transparent sheet over the exposed front portion of the cornea. Thus light must pass through the conjunctiva, the cornea, the aqueous humor, the lens, and the vitreous humor (a jellylike substance behind the lens) before it finally reaches the retina. The retina transforms the light into electrical impulses which are transmitted to the brain via the optic nerve. The brain then interprets these impulses and we "see."

The cornea, the conjunctiva, and the lens area all physiologically related to each other and to the skin and hair; they all derive from the ectodermal (outer) layer of the embryo in the early stages of its development. There were instances prior to the MER/29 triad of skin and hair changes followed by cataracts where drugs adversely affected the hair and skin as well as the lens.

Unlike hair and skin, which undergo constant regeneration, the lens does not. Newly formed lens cells do not replace old cells; rather they are added to the old, which are compressed into the lens' core. The lens, in some respects, thus resembles an onion with its many layers. If a lens cell should be damaged in one way or another so that it loses its transparency, it remains as a flaw in the lens forever. Often these flaws, or cataracts as they are called, are not sufficiently prominent to affect the over-all transparency of the lens, and vision is basically unimpaired. Sometimes, however, a large proportion of the cells are damaged, and the lens gradually loses its transparency as these opaque cells proliferate. When transparency is completely lost, light cannot pass through to the retina and the afflicted person or animal becomes blind. Surgical removal of the opaque lens is the only way cataract-caused blindness may be alleviated.

Although it was explained as "inflammatory" and not drug-related, the observation of corneal opacities in eight of twenty rats receiving 40 mg. of MER/29 per day was apparently regarded as significant by Merrell because they telephoned the FDA, and subsequently sent a confirming letter dated

February 29, 1960, to state that the corneal opacities which had been observed in the drugged rats "have now been found in the control animals." Furthermore, Merrell told the FDA that the findings were "discussed with our consultant, Dr. Joel G. Brunson [a friend of King] of the University of Mississippi Medical School, who advises that such corneal changes are common in the laboratory rat. Dr. Brunson has studied sections of the eyes of rats autopsied at Merrell and he feels that the changes are inflammatory and he reports the presence of acute inflammatory cells in the section." What Merrell did not tell the FDA was that as of February 24, 1960, they had observed corneal opacities in twenty-five out of thirty-six (not eight out of twenty) rats on the 40 mg. dosage, while only two out of thirty-eight control animals were so affected.

Merrell also reported on their dog experiments, in which groups of dogs were given dosages of 10, 25, and 40 mg. of MER/29 for four, six, and three months respectively. In the course of the studies several of the animals in Merrell's dog colony came down with distemper. While the dogs receiving 10 and 25 mg. of MER/29 were unaffected, one of the animals in the 40 mg. study was afflicted with the disease, necessitating a rerun of the tests. Accordingly, early in November 1959, five new beagles were conditioned and immunized. MER/29 affected these dogs very badly. Three of the five died before the expiration of the three months, and all had severely degenrated livers. Moreover, the two survivors (dogs 69 and 71) had cataracts. On the back of the autopsy sheet for dog 69 is the following notation in King's handwriting: "This animal when removed from the cage appeared to be blind. An opthalmascopic [*sic.*] examination of the eye reveal [*sic.*] an opacity of the crystalline lens and the retina was not visible. There was thick, viscous material externally in the eye. An eye and a section of the optic nv were taken for microscopic exam." A similar notation was on the back of the autopsy sheet for dog 71: "Animal appeared to have an eye infection. Opthalmascopic [*sic.*] examination revealed slight opacity to [illegible] lens and the retina was not clearly visible. Visual tests reveal that the animal could see."

Merrell told the FDA about the liver changes, but not the cataracts. While they later attempted to explain their failure to do so by contending that beagles get cataracts all the time or that the distemper outbreak might have had some effect (not only did the dogs not catch the disease and were immunized against it, but distemper does not even cause cataracts) and thus the observations were not "significant" or "reliable," there was never a convincing reason given why they reported the liver and not the eye changes. Certainly the report of the liver changes was far more damaging than the cataract report would have been, as their statement that beagles are prone to cataracts is true. Former judge Lawrence E. Walsh, who defended Merrell in some of the trials, perhaps summed it up best when he commented that he had "no explanation for this stupidity."

Nothing further was heard about the cataracts in the dogs until after the MER/29 bubble burst some two years later. There was, however, a puzzling indirect reference, apparently to these dogs, in Merrell's files. On March 18, 1960, Merrell's advertising agency sent over some questions it had with respect to the preparation of a promotional brochure. Among other things, it wanted to know "about the corneal changes recently noted in dogs." Merrell replied, "There are none." It did not mention the cataracts.

In May 1960, a month after MER/29's New Drug Application had been approved but before the drug was marketed, the FDA received a letter from a Dr. Lauretta E. Fox, who was at the time associate professor of pharmacology at the University of Florida. Dr. Fox reported that she had administered MER/29 to rats and had observed an "opaque cornea" and cataracts in the eyes of three of the six rats receiving the drug and a special high cholesterol diet. She pointed out that although she had not yet studied the tissue she felt that "further inquiries into the actions of this drug are needed."

By letter dated June 29, Dr. Frank J. Talbot, who had succeeded Dr. Epstein as the FDA medical officer assigned to MER/29 when Epstein resigned in December 1959, told Merrell of Dr. Fox's experiment and requested their comment, noting that "it would appear advisable that this study be repeated in order that the findings be confirmed if possible and their significance further delineated."

On July 22, 1960, Dr. Murray forwarded King's analysis of Dr. Fox's comments to the FDA. In it he stated that they had "no evidence from our experience or from the literature that MER/29 would in itself produce [the eye changes repoted by Dr. Fox]." Furthermore, he argued, no eye changes had been observed in either the dog or the monkey, and although "thousands of rats have been involved in many different experiments with MER/29 here in our laboratories," eye changes were observed in "only one group of animals, in one experiment, at only one time." He therefore concluded that the opacities "occurred as a matter of chance" rather than as a result of the drug. In a letter written directly to Dr. Fox with a copy to the FDA, Merrell said that they found her study confusing, further noting that "our pathologist states that he has never seen such involvement of the lens [cataract]" and that the corneal opacity might be caused by "an infection."

Admittedly, the significance of Merrell's failure to report the true extent of the "corneal opacities" in the rats or to disclose the cataracts in dogs 69 and 71 has been magnified by that handy historical tool the "retrospectoscope." However, it is clear that when, on April 19, 1960, the FDA approved the general prescription sale of MER/29 "solely on the evidence of the safety" of the drug, it did not know the complete story. The evidence of safety, insofar as it was based on the animal studies, was in large measure distorted by Merrell's personnel. The distortions may have been deliberate and significant, as the grand jury and the injuried plaintiffs charged, or they may have been inconsequential results of what Van

Maanen termed a "lack of appreciation for details." It is most likely that at least some of them were the result of what former judge Lawrence E. Walsh had characterized as "silly" errors. Nevertheless, the FDA was given a false picture of how the animals actually reacted to the drug. No one knows whether, had the FDA been given an accurate picture, they would have required more proof of MER/29's safety before approving its sale. Certainly those in the FDA who did not want the drug released would have been given additional ammunition and might have prevailed.

They did not prevail, however, and many people suffered the agonizing torment of having their vision slowly fade into grayness. If the consequences of this "monkey business" were not so tragic, it could almost be a comedy of errors. Squashed bugs abounded in Merrell's garden, but they were apparently crushed not so much by evil design as by clod-footed researchers who never seemed to look where they were going in their haste to market a drug with the enormous profit potential of MER/29. They would prove to be even more careless—some would say callous—when MER/29's position was threatened by serious adverse reactions, notably MER/29-induced cataracts in humans.

5

People Business

"May I never see in the patient anything but a
fellow creature in pain." *

As important as animal studies are, they provide only an
approximate indication of how a new drug will react in humans. A drug's ultimate action in people can only be determined by giving it to people, and this is routinely done once
it has been shown to be both safe and effective in animals.
This phase of a new drug's evaluation is not performed directly by the drug company but by independent physicians,
known as clinical investigators, who devote a substantial
portion of their time to appraising experimental drugs in
humans.

The clinical investigator, who is usually associated with
a major hospital or clinic, tests new drugs in either healthy
volunteers (often prisoners or medical students, who are taught
to accept the role of guinea pig as part of their pre-profes-
sional responsibilities) or in patients with the illness that the
drug is designed to cure or alleviate. Unlike the average
doctor who attempts to treat his patients with accepted and
proven remedies, the clinical investigator operates at the very
frontiers of medical knowledge. Sometimes, the new drug will
pass the clinical trials and emerge from experimental status
as a proven and valuable therapeutic agent. Other times,
however, the experimental human work will demonstrate that

* From the Oath and Prayer of the twelfth-century rabbi and physician
Maimonides.

the new drug is not sufficiently effective in humans to be worth while or, more ominously, despite the prior animal studies to the contrary, the human trials will indicate that the drug is not safe.

The testing of new drugs on humans is always risky, and the clinical investigator is not only expected to select his patients with care and obtain their informed consent,° but both he and the pharmaceutical company must recognize that the foremost aim of medicine is to cure the person who is ill and they must therefore put the patient's welfare above all other considerations.

One of MER/29's most important clinical investigators was Dr. William Hollander, who headed a team of physicians and researchers at the Boston University School of Medicine. Dr. Hollander explained during the course of his testimony that his group gave their patients "purely experimental drugs" with the hope of "making new findings" and were not, he said, "interested in confirming other people's work." When asked whether his primary intent was "the treatment of these patients or the study of these patients," he replied: "Study. This is purely a research procedure." He later modified this harsh-sounding response by saying that his work entailed "both study and therapy."

The clinical studies that the Hollander group did with MER/29 were very important to Merrell. Of the 116 patients reported on in the original MER/29 New Drug Application, fifty were theirs, and Dr. Hollander was an emphatic booster of Merrell's new wonder drug. He was one of the few clinical investigators who addressed Merrell's June 1961 sales convention, which was sort of a promotional pep rally for the boys in the field. He had previously reported to Merrell that he foresaw the day when MER/29 would be given to everyone

° As a result of the 1962 Kefauver-Harris amendments to the Food and Drug laws, and over vehement opposition by the pharmaceutical industry, the patient's consent is now mandatory in most instances of drug experimentation in humans.

over thirty-five, like vitamins.* When suspicions were cast on the drug, he became one of its staunchest defenders, proclaiming its value at medical association meetings as well as in letters forwarded by Merrell to the FDA.

In one such letter, dated November 10, 1961 (after Merrell and he already knew of four reported cases of MER/29-induced cataracts), Dr. Hollander volunteered that he was "not at all disturbed by the possible side effects that have been reported by other groups since they appear to be rare and reversible after withdrawing the drug." He admitted, however, that it was "possible that in 2 of the 4 patients that you have on file, the lens opacities [cataracts] might have been related to the administration of MER/29," but that this could have been "avoided had the patient been followed carefully and the MER/29 discontinued when the first sign of hair loss or dermatitis had appeared." He concluded his testimonial by noting that MER/29 was the "first drug to offer a rational and practical approach to the treatment" of high cholesterol levels and that it had a "wide margin of safety when used carefully in the recommended dose."

Some four months earlier Dr. McMaster, the associate director of medical research overseeing MER/29's clinical work, wrote the following memorandum to Dr. Werner: "Hollander mentioned the matter of his consultation fee. You will recall that we have had him on a personal retainer amounting to $2,400 per year payable in 2 semi-annual installments. If we wish to maintain this relationship (which is apart from the Wilkins' grant), a payment of $1,200 is now due. My own feeling is that we can't afford to chance alienation of Hollander just now (perhaps I shouldn't regard this as blackmail). Certainly we need his help and counsel." The retainer was paid.

In keeping with their lack of interest "in confirming other

---

* Although his statement to this effect was memorialized in a Merrell memorandum, Dr. Hollander denied being able to recall it.

other people's work," Dr. Hollander's group was one of the first to study MER/29 in humans. As the drug became more widely known (although it had not yet been approved for general prescription sale), other physicians also wanted to test it on their patients. One of these was a Dr. Wong of Howard University in Washington, D.C. A memorandum dated April 29, 1959, from Dr. Thomas R. Blohm, the chief of Merrell's biochemistry laboratory, to the director of medical research discussed the advisability of complying with Dr. Wong's request for the drug. Blohm explained that Wong was "charged with controlling atherogenesis in some Pentagon generals" and that a number of them experienced elevated cholesterol levels "every time an interservice fight develops or a missile fails to leave the launching pad." Wong was "anxious to get MER/29 for clinical studies" and in order to "smooth out the bumps in their cholesterol curves." Dr. Blohm, however, was not so sure that this was a good idea, explaining that he "would hesitate to use any new drug in those very valuable people." However, he noted that "Dr. Wong claims to have other patients and facilities which may be of interest to us," namely that he "gets an unusually high percentage of permissions for autopsy on negro hospital patients, so that he could help us assess effects of MER/29 on human atherosclerosis and tissue unsaponifiable matter."

This hesitancy to "use any new drug," and MER/29 specifically, evidently did not extend to those people not considered "very valuable," for MER/29 was not only given to several thousand people before it was approved by the Food and Drug Administration, including presumably those "negro hospital patients" Dr. Wong evidently felt confident he could autopsy, but Merrell sanctioned human experimentation with the drug even though they did not expect to receive any useful information in return.

On May 20, 1959, one of Merrell's vice-presidents, Robert H. Woodward, wrote to president Getman stating that some military hospitals had been asked to do experimental work with MER/29. Woodward explained that they "were not thinking here so much of honest clinical work" as they were of "pre-marketing softening prior to the introduction of the product."

In another instance, Dr. McMaster recommended that a grant of $500 be given to Dr. Hyman Engelberg of the Cedars of Lebanon Hospital in Los Angeles in order to delay the publication of what McMaster feared would be an adverse report on work which Dr. Engelberg had already done with MER/29. As McMaster explained it, "Although it begins to appear that any report from this study may be a negative one, we may find that we are money ahead to keep Dr. Engelberg busy at it for a while longer rather than to take a chance on his reporting negatively on so few patients." After noting that he thought Dr. Engelberg was using analysis technique which was "in some disfavor," McMaster emphasized that it was his "personal recommendation" that "the grant-in-aid be approved only to keep Dr. Engelberg occupied for a while longer." When asked about this at one of the trials, Dr. McMaster admitted that he "did not believe that this study would lead to anything productive" but stated that he recommended that the grant be approved nevertheless because he "thought it would be better not to make an enemy out of Dr. Engelberg."

Merrell's original MER/29 submission to the FDA reported that clinical studies in the 116 patients demonstrated that the drug reduced cholesterol levels in most and was apparently safe. The only observed side effects were isolated cases of nausea, heartburn, and rash. Merrell also reported that the drug increased the tolerance for exercise in some patients with heart disease. The company was obviously delighted and naturally anticipated quick FDA approval.

It was not forthcoming. The FDA noted that most of the patients were on MER/29 for comparatively short periods of time (the longest was six months), and although a number of them received large dosages, the FDA felt that there was insufficient proof that the drug, intended for chronic use, was safe over the long term. Accordingly, it required that additional animal tests be run. Merrell acquiesced, and in February 1960 they reported on the rat and dog experiments which we have already examined. While they failed to inform the FDA that two of the high-dose male beagles developed cataracts, they did report that the dogs underwent massive liver degeneration. Although it is hard to judge at this point in time what effect disclosure of the cataracts would have had on MER/29's New Drug Application, the effect of the liver-damage report was cataclysmic, at least initially.

Major concern about MER/29 focused on the liver because the drug inhibited that organ from manufacturing cholesterol, and many wondered whether its other functions would be similarly altered. An FDA staff memorandum submitted to Dr. Talbot on February 23, 1960, ominously noted that all the reported animal studies indicated that MER/29 was "producing toxic effects" at "relatively low dosages" and that there was "little margin of safety with the drug." Furthermore, because it was not known whether reducing cholesterol levels was actually beneficial, it was felt that MER/29 was "potentially" too toxic for widespread use. The memorandum concluded by recommending that before MER/29's New Drug Application was approved, "the company should submit results of well controlled extensive clinical studies in which the individuals have received the drug for periods of several years."

On March 7, 1960, representatives from Merrell met with the FDA in an attempt to defuse its concern. They were unsuccessful. On March 28 Dr. Talbot wrote to Merrell stating that "because of the potential hazard of liver toxicity with this drug, and further because of the highly theoretical value of taking such a drug as MER/29 (to our minds)," * the NDA

---

* This parenthetical reference to the simmering medical dispute of whether high cholesterol is a cause of atherosclerosis resulted in one of the most damaging memoranda discovered in Merrell's files. It was dated April 1,

would not be approved until "longer term" human trials indicated that it was safe.

Merrell was not to be put off. They wanted MER/29 on the market as soon as possible, and they were not going to allow any delay if they could possibly help it. On March 31 they forwarded a three-and-one-half-page summary of liver-function studies for 221 of the patients who had been given MER/29 experimentally up to that point (there were thousands) and argued that these results "established beyond reasonable doubt that MER/29 produces no alterations in hepatic [liver] functions in man."

The Food and Drug Administration reversed itself. A history of its relationship with Merrell concerning MER/29, prepared by the FDA for a Senate investigating committee, notes that after the FDA received what it termed, somewhat misleadingly, a "detailed" summary of the liver-function studies on the 221 patients, and since the monkey study "had likewise shown a total absence of toxicity," it concluded that the drug "was safe for use under the conditions set forth in the New Drug Application." A formal letter of approval was sent on April 19, 1960.°

MER/29 was thus approved less than three weeks after the FDA had demanded that human studies be done to show that the drug, intended for long-term use, was not toxic over the long term. The FDA did require, however, that Merrell

---

1960, and was written by the director of research, Dr. Harold Werner, to Merrell's top officers including president Getman. Although fairly innocuous in content, it complained that the FDA's balancing of effectiveness against toxicity was not legally permissible and that the FDA was "acting as God Almighty in deciding whether or not one has a right to develop brand new types of therapy based on a theory which in this case happens not to appeal to our friends at the Food and Drug Administration." The memorandum was headed READ AND DESTROY. It was effectively used by plaintiffs' lawyers in attacking Merrell's credibility: they asked time and time again what other memoranda were so labeled and *were* destroyed.

° A memorandum dated April 1, 1960, written by Robert Woodward, a Merrell vice-president, begins by noting that "we have obtained our effective NDA on MER/29." The FDA must therefore have notified Merrell it was approving the drug well before the formal letter was sent.

warn physicians that the "long-term" or lifetime effects of [MER/29] are unknown" and that while "clinical liver damage has not been encountered, periodic liver function tests may be desirable until more long-term safety data are available."

We may never know the real reason the FDA changed its position. Dr. Talbot noted in an interview with a reporter for the Washington *Sunday Star* in August 1962 that Merrell, "anxious to promote" MER/29 at a forthcoming AMA convention, kept bombarding him with arguments (they "like to keep the pressure on," he recalled) and that finally he "released the drug with the knowledge that things might appear later which were not obvious at the time." Unfortunately his intuition was to prove correct. On April 17, 1962, almost precisely two years to the day after Dr. Talbot wrote Merrell informing them that MER/29's New Drug Application was being approved "solely on the evidence of the safety of the drug," Merrell's president sent the following letter to every physician in the nation:

Dear Doctor:

This letter is to inform you of the Merrell decision to withdraw MER/29 (triparanol) from the market. We are today, with the cooperation of the Food and Drug Administration, asking all hospital and retail pharmacies as well as other possible outlets to return immediately their total stock of this drug.

This decision is based on additional reports of side effects of the kind reported to you in our letter of December 1, 1961 [mainly cataracts], some of which have occurred at usual dosage. It is recommended that you have your patients discontinue use of MER/29.

As you probably know, Merrell has had and will continue to have an extensive research program in cardiovascular disease. MER/29 has been one important phase of this effort. The work on this compound by us and many others has made contributions to basic knowledge in this field.

We would appreciate any data you may be able to furnish us concerning your own past experience with this drug. Such data are most useful when supplied in case history form.

Sincerely yours,
Frank N. Getman

This sad epistle was a far cry from an earlier letter Getman had directed to the nation's physicians, in May 1960. Describing it as "certainly one of my happiest duties," he announced that "MER/29, a unique compound which inhibits the formation of excess cholesterol in the body, will be available for prescription" around the first of June. Noting that he was "very proud" to be able to make the announcement, Getman expressed his "earnest hope that in your hands MER/29 may indeed prove a step forward in our common struggle against cardiovascular disease." He did not tell them that Merrell was marketing the drug not only before the ultimate effect of MER/29 on the liver was known but even though the company knew it was causing the accumulation of another fatty substance, desmosterol, in the blood.

The body manufactures cholesterol in a long and complicated process. The basic raw material is a comparatively simple molecule which is transformed, by numerous alchemic manipulations, into desmosterol and then cholesterol. Papers presented at Merrell's December 1959 Princeton Conference by a team of National Heart Institute researchers headed by Drs. Daniel Steinberg (M.D.) and Joel Avigan (Ph.D.) confirmed what Merrell had suspected as early as January: that MER/29 worked by inhibiting desmosterol's conversion into cholesterol. While desmosterol is normally a transient compound in the body, being almost immediately transformed into cholesterol, they found it had accumulated in significant quantities in MER/29-treated rats and humans.

Dr. Steinberg was worried. On December 28, less than two weeks after the Princeton Conference, he wrote Dr. McMaster stating that while he recognized that Merrell was "anxious to obtain FDA approval to market the drug," he did "not feel that this would be wise" until it was known just what desmosterol did to the body. If, for example, desmosterol could cause atherosclerosis as cholesterol was thought to do, MER/29 would then be merely substituting one dangerous substance for another.

A week later Dr. McMaster replied, arguing that all the evidence demonstrated that desmosterol was not harmful. Dr. Steinberg was not convinced. Still clearly worried, he told Dr. McMaster that the only way they could be certain was by continuing "long-term studies of the drug in animals and selected patients." As he wrote to another Merrell scientist in the middle of January 1960, he felt that in view of the desmosterol enigma, "general use [of MER/29] is not warranted at the present time."

But Merrell was not to be delayed. It would market the drug first and ask questions later—an attitude which had previously been reflected in its September 24, 1959, letter to the FDA in which the company objected to the delay in approving MER/29 pending further studies and expressed its willingness "to withdraw the product from the market if real toxicity problems" were later uncovered in the course of additional tests.° Despite the serious questions raised by Dr. Steinberg (who would later be accused by Dr. Van Maanen of "using MER/29 as a tool for his notorious fame"), the FDA was content to let Merrell market the drug so long as the package insert warned that "greater than normal quantities of desmosterol can be qualitatively shown in the livers and blood of animals and the blood of human beings treated with MER/29" and that the "significance of the presence of this substance is unknown and speculative."

Although desmosterol's significance was originally "unknown and speculative," scientists later learned that, like cholesterol, it forms on the inside of the arterial walls. In

---

° Withdrawal of the drug was evidently always considered a possibility. In a memorandum dated May 17, 1960, from one top Richardson-Merrell officer to another, it was noted that the company had a drug closely related to MER/29 available "as a substitute in the event MER/29 gets into trouble."

most patients MER/29 reduced the levels of these two substances combined below the pretreatment level for cholesterol alone. Nevertheless, the appearance of desmosterol as even a partial substitute for cholesterol meant that MER/29 was not as effective as had been previously thought. After some prodding Merrell eventually changed its literature to reflect this view, but the record reveals a strange reluctance to acknowledge desmosterol as a problem. For example, when Merrell's advertising agency inquired in March 1960 as to whether a statement in an earlier brochure prepared for the clinical investigators that the "accumulation of cholesterol precursors [desmosterol is one] in the liver is highly unlikely, at least in rats" was still true, Merrell replied yes. This was some three months after Drs. Steinberg and Avigan had told the assembled conferees at the Princeton Inn just the contrary and was, in fact, contradicted by Merrell's FDA-approved warning.

As late as February 2, 1961, Merrell's president Frank Getman wrote to Robert Shelton, a semiretired officer who abstracted scientific reports for Merrell's hierarchy, that desmosterol was proving to be an "unwanted, troublesome problem," but that "all the evidence definitely indicates that it isn't harmful and, in fact, we theorize that it may be beneficial." Seven months later Shelton would confide to Getman that he had been "deleting" the name of Merrell's vice-president in charge of sales and marketing from the list of those receiving "recent articles on MER/29 since they continually bring up the point about desmosterol" and he thought that they "might be a little discouraging to him."

Another problem which Merrell apparently tried to gloss over was their suspicion that MER/29 might interfere with either conception or the healthy growth of the human fetus. In October 1959 Merrell's endocrinology laboratory reported that fertility studies in rats indicated that MER/29, in doses as low as 10 mg. for every kilogram of body weight, adversely affected the ability of the animal to successfully reproduce.

It therefore recommended "that MER/29 *not* be administered to women during pregnancy, and that it be limited to the recommended 250 mg.* daily dosage in premenopausal women." Something was lost in the transmission of this recommendation to the FDA. On February 4, 1960, Merrell requested approval to note in its MER/29 brochure that since "cholesterol plays an important role in the development of the fetus, the drug should not be administered during pregnancy." This warning, Merrell wrote, was being suggested "purely on theoretical grounds." No mention was made of the real reason for their concern.

Apparently the FDA did eventually learn of the rat experiment (although there is nothing in the record to indicate when), for on September 23, 1960, Dr. Talbot requested Merrell to make available additional information concerning fertility studies. He also indicated that although the MER/29 brochure warned against administering the drug during pregnancy, he believed the warning should be expanded to include all women of child-bearing age.

On October 7 Merrell admitted that "high doses of MER/29 interfere with conception in rats" but pointed out that "there is no evidence" that this occurs in humans. In support of this contention they reported that two women who had conceived while on MER/29 delivered normal and healthy babies and that they knew of another patient who had also conceived while on MER/29 and was then in her fourth month. Her doctor, Merrell wrote, "expects to keep this patient on therapy [despite the warning that since 'cholesterol plays an important role in the development of the fetus, the drug should not be administered during pregnancy'!] and will inform us of the outcome about 6 months from now."

Although most of the early concern focused on whether MER/29 damaged the liver, whether it interfered with conception, and whether desmosterol might prove to be harmful,

* This works out to from two to five milligrams per kilogram of body weight for most adults.

the drug's ultimate vice, the causing of skin and hair changes followed by cataracts, is barely hinted at in the first official catalogue of side effects encountered in the clinical trials. The original package insert stated: "MER/29 is well tolerated at a dose of 250 mg. daily. Infrequent side effects have occurred but their incidence is too low for positive correlation with the administration of the drug. Isolated reports have been received of nausea, vomiting, temporary vaginal bleeding and dermatitis." "Dermatitis," of course, referred to the few instances of rash and skin eruptions noticed by the clinical investigators.

No one knew at the time that, as the drug was taken by more and more people for longer periods of time, the cases of "dermatitis" would increase in number and severity, that patients' hair would lighten in color and then fall out, and that these reactions presaged the development of cataracts.

If Merrell had waited until they had more clinical experience with the drug, much of the ensuing suffering might have been avoided. They did not want to wait, however: MER/29's potential sales were too great. Nor did the FDA compel the company to wait, despite the staff opinion that the drug had "little margin of safety." Rather, as we have seen, it was content to allow MER/29 to be sold with the warning that the consequences of its long-term use were "unknown" and, as Dr. Talbot candidly admitted, "with the knowledge that things might appear later which were not obvious at the time."

Merrell's haste in getting MER/29 on the market recalls to mind what the noted heart specialist, and Dr. Hollander's superior at the Boston University School of Medicine, Dr. Robert W. Wilkins, told the gathered physicians and researchers at Merrell's Princeton Conference in December 1959. Several papers on MER/29's action in humans were read, and at the end of the session Dr. Wilkins was called upon to summarize what had been presented. In the course of his summary he noted that there had not been "sufficient experience" with the drug and that he found "drug companies reluctant to accept" the fact that "you cannot tell what a drug will do after four or five years of treatment without waiting four or five years." When Merrell abstracted the Princeton Conference proceedings and distributed the precis free to the medical profession, it deleted Dr. Wilkins' caveat and oblique condemnation.°

Merrell launched MER/29 by having Western Union distribute a looseleaf binder containing promotional material to some 160,000 physicians. In an accompanying memorandum Dr. McMaster stated that the binder was to "serve as a convenient repository" for additional material on MER/29, because it "is our intention to keep you fully informed on all aspects of its use." At one of the MER/29 trials, Richardson-Merrell's president, H. Robert Marschalk, testified that it was standard company policy for inquiries by physicians to be answered "objectively and promptly." Just how "objectively" these questions were answered and just how "fully informed" Merrell kept the medical profession will now be examined.

Standard medical textbooks indicate that the first subjective symptom of cataracts is a dim, hazy, or blurred vision. Sometimes the person with developing cataracts will see halos when looking into a bright light and fixed (as opposed to floating) spots before his eyes. Double vision is another common early complaint.† It is also important to remember that the lens, the cornea, and the conjunctiva of the eye and the hair and skin all develop from the ectodermal layer of the human embryo and that cataracts preceded by hair and skin

---

° Dr. Philip Lisan, one of the clinical investigators from the Hahnemann Medical College and Hospital in Philadelphia, similarly told his fellow conferees at the Princeton Inn that while he observed an "apparent improvement" in patients suffering from coronary and arterial insufficiency who had been given MER/29, the drug's true effect in this respect could only be determined after five or ten years. This statement too was deleted from the Merrell precis.

† See, e.g., *May's Diseases of the Eye* (22d ed., 1957), p. 264, and Kirby, *Surgery of Cataract* (1950), pp. 138 *et seq.*

changes were known in the medical literature prior to the MER/29 tragedy.

The first reports indicating that MER/29 may have been inducing side effects other than "dermatitis" were scattered. On October 16, 1959, Dr. John G. Freeman of the Nebraska Psychiatric Institute of the University of Nebraska, one of Merrell's clinical investigators (who, however, was not invited to the Princeton Conference), reported that some of his patients complained that their eyes were watering. Five months later, in March 1960, Dr. Freeman reported that their eyes were still watering and that one now complained of blurred vision. Dr. McMaster replied that he wondered if the side effects "could have been coincidental with the administration of drugs other than MER/29 concurrently?" He would later surmise that since MER/29 was "capable of producing an allergic type dermatitis" in some 2 percent of people taking the drug, it was conceivable that the watering of the eyes was being caused by the irritation of the conjunctiva.

In March 1960 Merrell received a report from another one of its investigators that two of his female patients taking MER/29 were suffering from "a marked dryness of the skin with scaling" and were also losing their hair. In April this same doctor reported that the hair of a male patient taking MER/29 was turning gray. In May, another clinical investigator wrote that several of his patients were complaining of itching eyelids and that one man's vision was blurred. He also told of a woman whose hair began to fall out after she had taken MER/29 for five months but regrew following its discontinuance. In August, Merrell received another complaint of blurred vision.

MER/29 had now been on the market for two months and was being actively promoted not only as an effective anticholesterol drug but as one which was "virtually nontoxic." At about this time Allen Toole, a forty-one-year-old father of two, went to his doctor for a physical checkup. His physician, Toole would later testify in his lawsuit against Richardson-Merrell, "decided that it would probably be for my own best interest to take a drug to lower the cholesterol level in my blood." The doctor prescribed MER/29.

The rest of 1960 was generally placid. While additional complaints of hair and skin trouble continued to trickle in, many physicians were enthusiastically prescribing MER/29. One of the few precautionary notes was sounded in the October 14 issue of *The Medical Letter*, a respected nonprofit publication which evaluates new drugs and medical techniques for physicians. While noting that MER/29 might prove to be valuable, it cautioned against excessive optimism and warned that the drug "should still be reserved for experimental trial."

Although two of Merrell's dogs had developed cataracts (which were not reported) and "opacities" had been observed in the eyes of rats (they had undergone skin and fur changes as well °) the company apparently did not yet see any connection with the human complaints. If they did, they told no one. Merrell was advising its salesmen to inform physicians who were reluctant to prescribe MER/29 that if anything developed which indicated that the drug was dangerous "we'd be the *first* to know it and *report it to you!*" The quiet was comforting, and every morning Allen Toole, like hundreds of thousands of other hopeful people, took one pearl-gray MER/29 capsule before breakfast.

The thunderclap presaging the storm came early in January 1961. Dr. Werner received a phone call from his counterpart at another drug company, Merck, Sharpe and Dohme, informing him that Merck had synthesized MER/29 in order to compare its effectiveness and safety with one of their own anti-cholesterol compounds and discovered that it gave their dogs and rats cataracts. Merrell was invited to the Merck

° Merrell laboratory sheets report observations of "odd coat" and "poor coat" for the rats receiving 40 mg. of MER/29.

laboratories to investigate, and on Friday January 20, 1961, Werner, Van Maanen, and King apprehensively traveled to West Point, Pennsylvania, to examine the Merck animals. Dr. Werner had prepared himself for the meeting by having Merrell's library compile an abstract of the literature dealing with drug-caused cataracts.

A memorandum prepared three days after the meeting by Dr. Harold M. Peck, Merck's director of toxicology and pathology, describes what happened. He noted that the Merrell group "appeared to accept" that the dog cataracts were caused by the drug but "were reluctant" to agree that the eye changes in the rats were cataracts * or that they were induced by MER/29. "They asked a number of questions," he reported, "in an attempt to find some factor other than drug treatment that would explain the development of cataracts in both dogs and rats."

King described to Merck some of Merrell's toxicology studies, mentioning that inflammatory corneal opacities had been observed in one rat experiment, but he neglected to tell them about the cataracts in the two dogs. Although Merrell would later contend that Merck's compound was not the same as MER/29, they never asked for a sample until their lawyers did so in August 1963. Neither did they suggest that the FDA be informed. Rather, they thanked Merck for the information and said they would attempt to duplicate the experiments. In his memorandum Dr. Peck noted that this would take more than six months and thought "that some action should be taken in the meantime." His superiors at Merck evidently disagreed, and they left it to Merrell's discretion whether to report the cataracts to the FDA. Merrell sat on the Merck study until late October until after MER/29 induced cataracts in humans had surfaced.

After Werner, Van Maanen, and King returned to Cincinnati they made arrangements for a rerun of Merck's study.

* Dr. Peck would later testify that cataracts in rats' eyes will often appear as corneal opacities to unskilled people.

King, however, while recognizing that this was the appropriate action to take, noted that the opacities in the rats' eyes were "similar" to those Merrell had observed in 1960 and disputed Merck's contention that they were true cataracts of the lens. Furthermore, while agreeing that Merck's dogs did have cataracts, he suspected that they might have been caused by inbreeding or malnutrition. In a memorandum dated January 26, 1961, to Dr. Van Maanen, King reassuringly wrote: "I would emphasize that our safety data to date on MER/29 is sound. The events of recent weeks have not lessened my confidence in the safety of MER/29 in any regard."

In the meantime Merrell was receiving additional MER/29 cautionary advice and complaints. Famed physiologist Dr. Ancel Keys (inventor of the K [for Keys]-ration) wrote Merrell that it was still "premature to push for widespread use of [MER/29] in the ordinary practice of medicine." On January 21, 1961, Dr. McMaster advised a physician who had gotten a rash while on MER/29 to discontinue the drug. On January 26, he admitted to another physician that hair loss "may be a drug side reaction in a few patients."

Then on February 1, 1961, another bolt of lightning struck. Dr. McMaster received a phone call from Dr. Eliot Corday, chief of cardiology at the Cedars of Lebanon Hospital in Los Angeles. Corday told McMaster that one of his patients who previously had undergone hair and skin changes while on MER/29 now had cataracts. Although Merrell would later pay Dr. Corday's patient $50,000 in settlement of his lawsuit, the company apparently did not think much of the report at the time and made no serious effort to learn more about it until Dr. McMaster visited Dr. Corday several months later. The company was now on notice, however, that MER/29 *might* produce cataracts in humans.

Two days after the Corday report one of Merrell's detailmen wrote that a patient on MER/29 had complained of having "a film over his eyes." * Merrell's director of professional relations, Dr. John B. Chewning, wrote to the physician asking for more information because the report was "unusual" and had not come to his attention before. Shortly thereafter Dr. Werner asked Merrell's library staff to research "the incidence of cataract in normal adults." In the third week of February a Texas physician named Alfons Salinger reported that a patient who had previously experienced severe skin reactions and whose hair had turned lighter in color and then began to fall out while on MER/29 was now complaining of a "burning sensation in the eyes" and that he "noticed a halo" whenever he looked into a bright light.†

A month later Merrell received the following note from one of their detailmen: "A pharmacist in my territory stated that when taking MER/29 for about a week or more his eyes started to tear and burn slightly. When therapy was discontinued these symptoms disappeared, but upon resuming MER/29 therapy he complained of the same problem. Do you have any information as to why he might be getting this reaction if it is possibly from MER/29?"

On March 21, 1961, Dr. Chewning's assistant, Dr. R. N. Puls, replied that he was "not aware of MER/29 producing such side effects" but that the complaint "appears to be an allergy-type reaction which, in the majority of patients on MER/29 experiencing such a reaction, has been in the form of a skin rash." Dr. Puls then protected his product, if not the pharmacist, admirably. He advised the detailman that it "would be wise before discontinuing therapy to be absolutely sure that the patient is not taking any other type of medication which might cause such tearing and burning." In August, although the company had gotten earlier complaints of blurred

* The ancients thought that the cataract was caused by a screen or shade which descended over the eye. See Kirby, *Surgery of Cataract* (1950), pp. 3-18.

† Although Merrell wouldn't learn about it until October, Dr. Salinger's patient developed cataracts.

vision, Dr. Puls would write to a physician that "we have received absolutely no reports of this type of reaction."

Dr. Puls was a young physician recently out of medical school, and for the few months he was with Merrell he worked as Dr. Chewning's assistant in the professional relations department. Part of his task was to answer physicians' questions in keeping with Merrell's pledge to keep them "fully informed" about MER/29. We have already seen how Dr. Puls was apparently unaware of the numerous eye complaints. He was also evidently kept in the dark about an April 28, 1961, complaint by a physician that MER/29 had caused a fatty degeneration of the liver in one of his patients, for on May 6 he wrote another physician that "at the present time we have received no reports of the drug causing fatty degeneration of the liver" and that he hoped "erroneous reports of fatty degeneration due to MER/29 do not deter you from further use of the drug, as I am sure it will continue to be a most valuable therapeutic tool in your practice."

On June 28, 1961, Dr. Puls wrote to a physician who was considering placing his wife on MER/29 therapy: "Let me assure you that in the thousands of patients that have been on MER/29, there have been absolutely no reports of liver toxicity." And on July 24 to another physician: "Let me assure you that we have received absolutely no reports of liver toxicity in patients taking MER/29 and this has been substantiated on a number of occasions by liver biopsy."

In one of the trials, former judge Lawrence Walsh, disclaiming any evil intent, acknowledged that Dr. Puls made "a couple of mistakes." Whether deliberate or not, Dr. Puls's approach was consistent with the way Merrell's salesmen were dircted to overcome physician resistance to MER/29. One instruction sheet for detailmen, entitled "Simple Question Counters 90% of Side Effect Questions," had this advice:

> We heard eight words the other day that neatly handle one of your biggest problems. When a doctor says your drug

causes a side effect, the immediate reply is: "Doctor, what other drug is the patient taking?"

Even if you know your drug can cause the side effect mentioned, chances are equally good the same effect is being caused by a second drug! You let your drug take the blame when you counter with a defensive answer. Know how to answer side effects honestly, yes, *but get the facts first.*

"Doctor, what other drugs is the patient taking? Been doing it for years? Why didn't you tell us then?"

In order to emphasize the point, the instruction sheet has a cartoon of a physician saying, "I guess it could have been the MAO inhibitor." (MAO inhibitors, which were designed to relieve depression, were known to cause skin reactions. When Dr. Corday originally complained that one of his patients— the one who ultimately got the cataracts—had a very bad skin condition which he thought was caused by MER/29, Dr. McMaster suggested that the MAO inhibitor the patient was also taking might have been at fault.)

In another directive distributed to the salesmen, a cartoon showed a doubting physician saying, "I don't know, Merrell, Dr. McCynic said it might be toxic." The detailmen were exhorted, "Don't let a few questioning doctors throw you!"

Although by March 1961 Merrell had already received some fifty reports that the hair of patients receiving MER/29 was turning a lighter color and falling out, Dr. McMaster wrote to a physician on March 20 that they were "not sure of a possible association." Three days later, however, in a confidential memorandum to Dr. Werner, he stated that it was the "feeling of the Department of Medical Research that there can be no doubt of the association of MER/29 therapy with the observed lightening, increased brittleness and loss of hair." He recommended that MER/29's side-effect warning be expanded to include "change in color, texture, or amount" of hair. On the next day Dr. McMaster's memorandum together with a supporting statistical compilation was trans-

SIMPLE QUESTION COUNTERS 90% OF SIDE EFFECT QUESTIONS

We heard eight words the other day that neatly handle one of your biggest problems. When a doctor says your drug causes a side effect, the immediate reply is: "Doctor, what other drug is the patient taking?"

Even if you know your drug can cause the side effect mentioned, chances are equally good the same effect is being caused by a second drug! You let your drug take the blame when you counter with a defensive answer. Know how to answer side effects honestly, yes, but get the facts first;

Doctor, what other drugs is the patient taking? Been doing it for years? Why didn't you tell us then?

TACE "LIFETIME OFFER" SELLS UROLOGISTS WHILE YOU CALL ON INTERNISTS AND GP's . . .

Personal letters from urologists all over the country indicate sincere interest in **TACE** and appreciation for samples you made available to them. For example:

> *Dear (Merrell):*
>
> *I want to thank you for the complimentary stock of TACE you sent for one of my needy patients, and for the kind offer to send a new supply when this becomes depleted.*
>
> *I will be glad to pass on to my patients the information about the economy of purchasing the 350 capsule size bottle.*
>
> *Sincerely yours,*
>
> *J.G.K., M.D.*

WHAT IS INFLUENCING **YOUR** MER/29 SALES?

THIS?

or **THIS?**

"I don't know, Merrell, Dr. McCynic said it may be toxic."

MER/29 already has more excellent clinical backing than most other drugs can ever claim. Don't let a few questioning doctors throw you! Know the answers ... Sell positively.

mitted to H. Smith Richardson, Jr., the forty-year-old president of Richardson-Merrell and grandson of its founder. The forwarding memorandum from Robert Woodward, a Merrell vice-president, explained that Merrell had reviewed the "reported thinning of the hair of people taking MER/29" and concluded that "we are morally and legally bound to include our findings in the side effects statement in the FDA approved brochure—even though the reported incidence is only 51 cases of roughly 300,000 treated."

> The reason for bringing this to your attention, Smith, is that we have made no changes to this point in any of our MER/29 literature, basically because we were afraid to "stir the pot" in Washington. We have heard from several sources that FDA at times has considered reopening our NDA file but, frankly, we do not know whether this is true. The risk we run in admitting this additional side effect must be realized, however, and weighed against our moral and legal obligations referred to earlier.
>
> Frank [Getman] and I both feel that the approach should be made. Further, we feel that to protect ourselves against possible damage suits, we should make the approach promptly. I thought it well to inform you, however, so that you may express your own opinion since, after all, the future of MER/29 is of interest to you and to others in the Enterprise as well as to Merrell.

Richardson's handwritten notes in the margins of Woodward's memorandum reflect his thinking on the matter. He wrote: "*Summary*—can expect publications on hair thinning, important to get brochure change before this happens. Also desirable to play ball with Talbot who got #29 through over protest. Talbot has authority to O.K." And then on the bottom, "Severe infections, dermatitis. Lawsuits."

On March 28 Smith Richardson, Jr., received another confidential memorandum, this time from Richardson-Merrell's chief scientist, and a former official with the FDA. After rehashing the various arguments for and against changing the warning statement, he summarized his views as follows:

I would say that the weight of the evidence seems to indicate that MER/29 may produce some hair changes in a very small proportion of cases. However, I do not believe it is fair to say that this is proven beyond any doubt. Nevertheless, I am inclined to go along with the recommendations of the Merrell group as I am sure that at least one or more of the physicians who have observed this effect on the hair of several of their patients during MER/29 therapy will publish their findings in the near future. I don't particularly like McMaster's suggested phrase "changes in color, texture, and amount," as this sounds rather frightening. After all, none of these cases developed green, pink or lavender hair, I hope. Therefore, I'm inclined to believe that Murray's simple phrase "thinning of the hair" should probably be sufficient. I believe it would be well also to stress the extremely low reported incidence of these hair changes.

The decision was made, and on April 6, 1961, Dr. Murray wrote to Dr. Talbot at the FDA. "Our attention has been called to several reports concerning thinning of hair," Murray said, "and while it is difficult to assess the importance of these reports (particularly since there have also been reports of increased hair growth*) we feel some mention should be made in our literature. Accordingly, we propose to modify the last sentence under 'side effects' in our existing brochure." The changed sentence read: "Isolated reports have been received of nausea, vomiting, temporary vaginal bleeding, dermatitis, and thinning of the hair." Dr. Murray's less frightening, if less accurate, phrase had been selected.

Dr. Talbot approved the change and, in accordance with FDA regulations, asked that copies of the revised brochure or package insert be sent as soon as they were printed. These were sent on June 5. The approved change, however, was prefaced with this sentence carried over from the earlier version: "Infrequent side effects have occurred but their

---

* The isolated reports that MER/29 induced regrowth in previously bald areas prompted Dr. Irving S. Wright, chairman of the Princeton Conference, to note, with unintended irony, that he was "intrigued by the first cure for baldness that I have encountered in the medical society in a long time and will be most interested to hear if anyone else has had that experience."

INTER-DEPARTMENT MEMO.

THE WM S. MERRELL COMPANY

47

To [Mr. H. Smith Richardson, Jr.   Date   March 24, 1961

From   R. W. Woodward

Copies to   F. N. Getman
             R. H. McMaster
             F. J. Murray
             H. W. Werner

Subject   MER/29 -- COMPLAINTS OF HAIR CHANGES

Summary - Can project pullgations on hair thinning, Important to get brochure change before this happens. Also desirable to play ball with Talbot who ... MER/29 wrong?

C O N F I D E N T I A L

Before Frank left for vacation, we had initiated a review of reported thinning of the hair of people taking MER/29. It is our feeling that we are morally and legally bound to include our findings in the side effects statement in the FDA approved brochure—even though the reported incidence is only 51 cases of roughly 300,000 treated.

one point that Talbot has only 5 - to O.K.

Attached for your review is a memo from Dr. McMaster setting forth the facts as we have them, together with a copy of a proposed letter to FDA by Joe Murray which has not yet been sent.

The reason for bringing this to your attention, Smith, is that we have made no changes to this point in any of our MER/29 literature, basically because we were afraid to 'stir the pot' in Washington. We have heard from several sources that FDA at times has considered reopening our NDA file but, frankly, we do not know whether this is true. The risk we run in admitting this additional side effect must be realized, however, and weighed against our moral and legal obligations referred to earlier.

Frank and I both feel that the approach should be made. Further, we feel that to protect ourselves against possible damage suits, we should make the approach promptly. I thought it well to inform you, however, so that you may express your own opinion since, after all, the future of MER/29 is of interest to you and to others in the Enterprise as well as to Merrell.

102630

RWW:mkm

New Eng Journal - adrenal hormones decreased .. 4 to 8 times recommended dose. Flat statement that at " " this does not occur. Severe infectious dermatitis. Lawsuits.

Handwritten notes by H. Smith Richardson, Jr., concerning MER/29 hair-loss warning.

incidence is too low for positive correlation with administration of the drug."

In the meantime the predictions of imminent publication of the side effects came true when, on April 26, 1961, a group of researchers at the Mayo Clinic published reports on several patients who had experienced hair loss and severe ichthyosis while on MER/29. Despite the earlier opinion of Merrell's medical research department that "there can be no doubt of the association of MER/29 therapy with the observed lightening, increased brittleness and loss of hair," Dr. Puls, on May 26, 1961, wrote to an inquiring physician that the "[Mayo] report dealing with loss of hair in a few patients taking MER/29 should not give rise to undue concern." He explained that while Merrell had "received a small number of reports of hair loss in conjunction with MER/29" therapy, "there is little substantial evidence to show a direct connection between this occurrence and the drug."

The FDA's Dr. Talbot was less sanguine. On June 20 he wrote to Merrell that in light of the Mayo report the FDA could not agree with Merrell's revised brochure that there was not a "positive correlation" between hair loss, ichthyosis, and MER/29. He also suggested that the side effects "should be described in a more comprehensive manner than just 'dermatitis, and thinning of the hair,' with a further recommendation for immediate discontinuance of the drug should such effects appear."

On August 2, 1961, Merrell submitted a revised brochure. The new side-effects paragraphs read as follows:

> MER/29 is well tolerated at a dose of 250 mg. daily. Occasionally reported side effects include dermatitis such as urticaria [rashlike eruption of the skin], and dryness and scaliness of the skin. When the latter has occurred, it has been after prolonged administration. Thinning or changes in color or texture of the hair have also been observed after several months of MER/29 therapy. These conditions appear to be reversible and if they are observed, immediate drug discontinuance is recommended.

There have been isolated reports of nausea and vomiting, but administration at mealtime usually eliminates this complaint.

Dr. Talbot left the FDA in September without approving the revised brochure. He was succeeded as the medical officer in charge of the MER/29 NDA by Dr. John O. Nestor, and he never approved the revision either. The recommendation to discontinue the drug if hair or skin changes were observed would not be conveyed to the medical profession until December 1, 1961.

Merrell has consistently contended that the FDA exacerbated the cataract problem by not approving the August 2 revision and by not approving a letter which they drafted in the second week of October warning that lens "opacities" might result if the drug was not discontinued after the hair or skin changes were observed. Dr. Nestor testified that he considered the draft warning-letters which Merrell prepared to be "inadequate" and feared that they might mislead the physician rather than warn him. While this is strongly controverted by Merrell, it appears clear that the company could have alerted the medical profession on its own, without the FDA's approval—if only by taking out advertisements in medical journals. Such advertisements, as Getman would later admit, were not then under the jurisdiction of the Food and Drug Administration.

In any event, if Merrell had truly wished to warn the medical profession as to the danger of cataracts, they could have done so first and fought the FDA (if that developed) later. This they did not choose to do. And they continued to be less than candid in responding to inquiring physicians. We recall that when Dr. Puls, on August 1, 1961, wrote that Merrell had "received absolutely no reports" of blurred vision, there were at least three such reports. Merrell was also informed of a patient who complained that MER/29 caused a "film" to form over his eyes. In June a clinical investigator who had been experimenting with large doses of MER/29 reported that a medical student to whom he had given the drug for three weeks had developed an inflammation of the iris after first experiencing hair and skin changes. Furthermore, as we have seen, the company was directly aware that the drug might cause cataracts, not only in animals (their two 1960 dogs and Merck's dogs and rats) but in humans as well. Shortly after Dr. Corday's report that his patient had developed cataracts while on MER/29, Dr. Werner requested Merrell's librarian to research "the incidence of cataract in normal adults." Nevertheless, on August 4, Dr. McMaster wrote in response to a complaint of double vision that he was "unable" to explain the observation. He noted that it was the "first instance of this sort about which we have heard" and that "nothing in the animal studies provides data which might shed light on it." Dr. McMaster did recommend, however, that the drug be discontinued.

Although it was meeting with some resistance from the "Dr. McCynics" who heeded *The Medical Letter*'s warning, and despite the FDA-approved cautionary statement in the MER/29 brochure that the drug's long-term safety was still unknown, Merrell continued to vigorously promote MER/29. The May 4, 1961, issue of *$ales Talk,* a chatty newsletter for salesmen, told of an effective way to persuade reluctant physicians to prescribe the drug:

> When doctors say "MER/29 long-term effects unknown," how long is long?
> Many Merrellmen have reported that a common "hedge" doctors use for not prescribing MER/29 is the [FDA required] phrase, "Long-term effects are unknown."
> The following quote from a letter written by Dr. Bob McMaster to a doctor who made this statement demonstrates a good positive answer for these doubters:
> "The animal work with MER/29 has now been in continuous study for more than five years. Clinical study has been in progress for about three years. Many of the patients who were included in the original studies are still being carried on the drug so that safety data are available in several hundreds of patients who have now taken it for periods in excess of two years."

Two weeks later the American Medical Association's Council on Drugs would conclude its evaluation of MER/29 by warning that "much longer and more careful clinical [human] studies must be performed before the drug can be considered safe for general or long-term use." In June 1961, Merrell's salesmen were flatly told that "MER/29 is a safe drug for long-term use."

Shortly thereafter, Allen Toole, who had now been off and on MER/29 for about a year, noticed that the hair on his legs disappeared and they "got very, very smooth." Later his skin would become "quite irritated, and quite painful at times," so that he would have to wear cotton pajamas under his trousers to keep wool clothing from coming in contact with his raw, inflamed skin. Although apparently neither Toole nor his physician had yet associated his loss of hair and painful skin condition with MER/29, others similarly affected did.

On September 25, 1961, a Merrell detailman sent the following urgent message to Cincinnati: "Friday evening 9-22-61 7:30 pm I was contacted on the phone by an unidentified party (woman) stating that she had been on MER/29 for approx. 8 months and that she had lost half her hair on her head. She wouldn't give name or M.D. but said she would call later (or her attorney). Saturday morning I checked with ½ doz. drugstores and found two patients had returned MER/29 bottles by doctor's instruction, for credit." Their physicians had directed them to stop taking the drug because they were losing their hair. The detailman gloomily noted that "the bad thing about these reports is that our competition has gotten hold of this info—and are playing it up with the M.D.s. I've noticed a slowdown on MER/29 sales for past two–three weeks. And Friday I found out why." On October 12 Dr. McMaster told the detailman "not to get panicky" and assured him that the company was "planning shortly to provide additional information about hair and skin effects from the drug to all people in the field force."

Meanwhile, as Toole, like many others, continued to take his little pearl-gray MER/29 capsule before breakfast, Merrell's rerun of the Merck rat and dog studies was beginning to confirm Merck's findings. The experiment was barely a few months old when Merrell noticed what they termed "eye opacities" in the rats. The laboratory sheets reported that their general appearance was "good—except for loss of hair and sight." By late September nearly all the female rats receiving 40 mg. of MER/29 plus a special diet supplemented with cholesterol and vitamins had "opacities," while some 70 percent of the males on that regimen were similarly affected. Sixty percent of all rats receiving 40 mg. of the drug without a supplement also developed the eye trouble. These results were never reported to the FDA. Dr. Van Maanen would later testify that there was no need to do so because the FDA had been previously told of corneal opacities in the 1960 rats and these findings did not add anything significant.

The argument is faulty in two respects. First, it will be remembered that Merrell contended that in the 1960 tests the eye opacities in rats were "inflammatory" and were therefore unrelated to MER/29. This new finding of opaque corneas in MER/29-treated rats should have been disclosed. Secondly, there is strong evidence, despite Merrell's repeated insistence to the contrary, that the 1961 rats actually developed opaque lenses (cataracts) rather than opaque corneas. If this was the case, then there can be no doubt that this confirmation of Merck's finding that MER/29 can cause cataracts in rats should have been reported to the FDA. The evidence that MER/29 gave the rats true cataracts is in a February 1962 letter written by Dr. Van Maanen. The critical paragraph reads as follows:

> In rats the earliest observations of cataracts was made after three months administration of 40mg/kg/day of [MER/29]. After administration of [MER/29] for five months [it was now September 1961!] the incidence was approximately 75%. It appears that female rats are more susceptible to cataract

development than male rats. On the other hand, female rats barely tolerate this high dose of [MER/29].

In addition to the eye "opacities" which Merrell observed in the rats (but did not report), by October 18 they found that all four surviving dogs who received 40 mg. of MER/29 and all three surviving dogs who received 40 mg. of the drug plus the cholesterol and vitamin supplement also developed cataracts. Although Merrell told the FDA that only one dog got cataracts, the significance of the animal experiment was by now becoming academic. For on Saturday morning October 7, Merrell's director of medical research, Dr. Carl Bunde, received a phone call from the Mayo Clinic and was told that two of the patients who had earlier been reported as suffering hair and skin changes now had cataracts. This was the second and third report of cataracts in humans taking MER/29 which Merrell received. At the World Series game that afternoon Dr. Bunde told Dr. McMaster the bad news. Their day was not made any brighter by Cincinnati's 3-2 loss to the New York Yankees.

On Monday Dr. McMaster called Dr. Richard W. P. Achor at the Mayo Clinic for additional information and decided to fly to Rochester, Minnesota, on Wednesday. Once at Mayo he was given the case histories of the two patients and was told of another man, a Texas dentist, who had also developed cataracts following what he alleged to be MER/29-induced hair and skin changes. This was the same case which Dr. Salinger had reported on in February 1961, noting at that time that his patient was complaining of burning eyes, halo vision, a severe skin condition, and increasing baldness.* Merrell now knew of four cataract cases.

---

* Associate director of medical research D. M. Bowles discussed Dr. Salinger's case with him. In a confidential memorandum dated October 23, 1961, directed to Dr. Bunde, Bowles reported that while Dr. Salinger believed that his patient's hair and skin problems were caused by the drug, he "questioned the relationship of the cataracts to MER/29 therapy." Bowles volunteered that he did nothing to disabuse Dr. Salinger of his doubts: "I made no mention of the fact that we have received reports of other patients on MER/29 having developed cataracts."

EYE OPACITY OF RATS RECEIVING 40 mg/kg/day OF MER-29 ORALLY

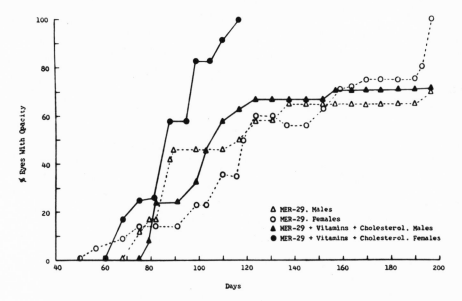

Merrell chart showing the percentage of rats receiving MER/29 alone and MER/29 plus vitamins and cholesterol with what they termed eye opacities. The study was started in April 1961 and was designed to check Merck's results. An attached memorandum, dated November 15, 1961, noted that there were "no eye changes in the controls."

When Dr. McMaster returned to Cincinnati a letter was drafted warning physicians to discontinue the drug if hair and skin changes were observed. On October 18 Dr. Murray called Dr. Nestor, told him about Mayo's report, and read the draft of Merrell's letter. He wanted the FDA's approval. This was the FDA's first indication that MER/29 might be causing cataracts in humans, and Dr. Nestor naturally wanted some time to think it over. At 8:40 the next morning he called Dr. Murray and told him that he did not have enough information to approve the letter. He said he suspected that the side effects might be more severe than were stated and that therefore the letter might "be misleading" and lull physicians into "a false sense of security." A meeting was arranged for October 26, to work things out. Nestor told Murray to bring everything which might have a bearing on the drug's toxicity.

Although they were thwarted in their attempt to send a warning letter to the general medical list, Merrell did not have to seek the FDA's prior approval to send such a letter to MER/29's clinical investigators. Accordingly, it was mailed to them on October 19, over the signature of Dr. Bunde, and read in part: "Four patients on long-term therapy [with MER/29] have now developed eye defects described as multiple small opacities on the posterior lens surface. All of these first had a severe long-lasting dermatitis and hair loss as well as changes in color and texture of hair." The letter strongly urged that the investigators "discontinue the drug if either hair or skin changes appear."

Despite Merrell's stated desire to alert the medical profession to the possibility of eye trouble, they were apparently still reluctant to take any action which might lead to direct proof that MER/29 was the cause. On October 12, 1961, they were considering a researcher's request for some radioactive MER/29, which he wanted to apply to the corneas of animals to determine if the drug would penetrate to the internal eye structure, where it might be of some benefit in the treatment of atherosclerosis of the retina. Dr. Blohm, the head of Merrell's biochemistry laboratory, concluded that "such a study at this particular time could be extremely dangerous to us" and would therefore "certainly recommend doing everything reasonable to discourage him from carrying out this study." A handwritten note by Dr. Bunde, Merrell's director of medical research, asked, "Do you think [MER/29] is directly toxic to the eye?" Dr. Blohm replied, similarly in a handwritten note, "I don't know, but it is irritating s.c. [subcutaneously, i.e., when applied directly under the skin]. It looks like my worries may be getting sort of academic anyhow. I just don't like the whole idea at this particular time because of the general eye problem."

While Merrell and the FDA were worrying about the growing problem with MER/29, Dr. McMaster and Dr. Nestor attended a convention of the American Heart Association in Miami, Florida over the weekend of October 20. They did not know each other but, as fate would have it, they met accidentally. Dr. McMaster later testified that he saw a man whose name tag identified him as Dr. John O. Nestor of the Food and Drug Administration and went over and introduced himself. They talked briefly about the two Mayo cataract cases, and when Dr. McMaster mentioned that Drs. Achor and Berge (also from Mayo) were at the convention Dr. Nestor said he wanted to meet with them. Dr. McMaster promised to set it up.

The meeting took place Sunday morning in Dr. McMaster's hotel room. Over breakfast, the two Mayo physicians described the cataracts, and Dr. Achor indicated that it was his personal feeling that they were caused by MER/29. Dr. Nestor testified that Drs. Achor and Berge told him after the meeting that they thought MER/29 should be withdrawn from the market and its use limited to research studies.

On Monday morning, October 23, after Nestor had returned to Washington he fired off an air mail special delivery letter to Dr. McMaster in which he reiterated that the October 26 meeting "must include a detailed discussion of all that is known from both experimental and clinical studies concerning the toxicity of MER/29." Dr. Nestor explained that since "your labeling and promotional literature has repeatedly stressed the freedom from major side-effects and lack of danger connected with the use of this drug, we feel that it is now necessary for you to give us the complete background information to date" including "all the information concerning eye changes in humans and animals with reference to both corneal and lenticular (cataracts) changes."

In preparation for the meeting Dr. Nestor received a detailed report from the FDA's Bureau of Program Planning and Appraisal showing that Merrell's claims for MER/29 were exaggerated. The report stated, among other things, that Merrell's contention that MER/29 reduces cholesterol "more than 20 percent below pretreatment levels in at least 80 percent of patients" was "totally unwarranted" and was "an excessive overclaim." It pointed out that, using figures submitted by Merrell's own clinical investigators, less than half of the MER/29-treated patients "had drops in their serum cholesterol levels of 20 percent or more below their pretreatment levels."

Merrell president Frank Getman later justified the claims by explaining that in calculating the percentage response in patients treated with MER/29, Merrell omitted all those patients who did not respond to the drug at all. There was thus a greater than 20 percent reduction in cholesterol levels in 80 percent of the *remaining* patients.

While Dr. Nestor was reviewing the MER/29 file, Merrell was busily gathering documents and working out a strategy for the October 26 meeting. The man in charge of collecting the documents for submission to the FDA was Dr. Murray. He later testified that he merely acted as a conduit, that he very rarely read any of the papers which passed through his hands and he "didn't read any of the toxicology reports" at all. When asked whether, in his capacity as Merrell's liaison with the FDA, he would have been concerned with reports that might have to be corrected in order to "keep on good relations with the Government," he replied, "Not at that particular time . . . our relations were pretty well shot as of October." He complained that the FDA had decreed that "scientific judgment" was no longer permissible and that therefore Merrell had "sent every scrap of paper we had."

Strategy was made at a higher level. Two days before the meeting Getman wrote a pessimistic memorandum to H. Robert Marschalk, who had recently succeeded Smith Richardson, Jr., as president of Richardson-Merrell (Richardson became chairman of Richardson-Merrell's board of directors). The subject matter of the memorandum was the appropriate course of action to take if the FDA announced it was going to seek suspension of MER/29's New Drug Application. Getman proposed drafts of two press releases. The first one, used "in the event of rumor that the FDA is about to suspend the NDA," read: "We have not received notice of any such hearing, as provided in the law. We are not in a position to comment until we do—if we do." The second, to be used if they actually received notice of a hearing, read:

> The Wm. S. Merrell Company, Division of Richardson-Merrell Inc., has today received a notice of hearing from the Federal Food and Drug Administration to determine whether its effective New Drug Application on MER/29 should be suspended. In our opinion such suspension would be unwarranted and unnecessary, and we believe that evidence presented at the hearing will sustain this position, stated H. R. Marschalk, president of Richardson-Merrell (or Frank Getman, president of The Wm. S. Merrell Company Division).

"Admittedly, the latter announcement is extremely brief," Getman added, "but I am proposing it in this form for two reasons—the first is that the less said, the better, as long as it adequately covers our position—and secondly, it is hard to give added reasons until we get the notice of hearing, which is similar to a complaint and outlines the reasons why the NDA should be suspended. If it should claim we withheld evidence, that would call for one type of statement, whereas if it were based on certain kinds of toxicity, it would call for another." This is one of the few indications that Merrell's top management was aware that the FDA might have suspected the company was not reporting everything. Getman's gloomy communication to his superior ended with this postscript: "Needless to say, our preparation for the Thursday meeting is going on at full speed."

The meeting took place in Dr. Nestor's office in Washington, with Merrell represented by director of research Werner;

director of medical research Bunde and his assistant Dr. McMaster; director of biological sciences Van Maanen; Dr. Blohm, head of the biochemistry laboratory; and Dr. Murray. Nestor would later testify, "I was really handicapped because I was one against six, and sometimes we were all talking at one time." They discussed the four known cataract cases, and Merrell attempted to tell Dr. Nestor about Merck's experiment, but without naming Merck. Nestor declined to receive an anonymous report, and Merrell said they would seek to get the company's permission. They then presented the following revised draft of the warning letter they had wanted to mail on October 18:

> Dear Doctor:
> The purpose of this letter is to advise you of those cases where MER/29 therapy should be discontinued. The types of cases where the drug is to be withdrawn were not apparent from the several thousand clinical cases studied during the two-year period prior to marketing of MER/29. These cases have recently been observed following the widespread use of MER/29.
> There have been a number of reports of hair loss, changes in color and texture of hair, and dermatitis. More recently, lens opacities have been observed in four patients following severe dermatitis.
> MER/29 should be immediately withdrawn if changes in hair or skin occur.
> Your patients should be informed to watch for hair and skin changes and directed to stop therapy and report to you if they should occur.
> For your information, the dermatitis usually is a dry, scaly type which may be associated with mild itching. It regresses following discontinuation of the drug. In a few patients, this mild dermatitis has progressed to a more severe ichthyoid type, which is the type in which the four cases of lenticular changes have been reported. This has only occurred when drug therapy has continued for a period after the dermatitis has appeared.
> The hair loss consists of a diffuse thinning, unlike alopecia areata or totalis [localized or total baldness]. In some cases, hair loss has become extensive; and in a few of these, the

thinning has involved body regions other than the scalp. Regrowth of hair occurs after varying periods of time following discontinuance of therapy.

This letter is sent as part of our continuing policy of fully informing the medical profession about MER/29. Your adherence to the cautions presented here will permit you to use MER/29 effectively in your practice.

Sincerely,

Carl A. Bunde, Ph.D., M.D.
Director of Medical Research

Dr. Nestor considered this letter, like the one which had been read to him over the phone on October 18, to be "inadequate" and it was not approved.

Meanwhile, Merrell's advertisements continued to herald MER/29's safety. The final regular addition to the MER/29 looseleaf binder, issued in late October 1961 (it had been printed in September), reiterated that keeping cholesterol levels down was "necessarily long-term therapy" and that "for such long-term therapy, MER/29 offers the advantages of demonstrated efficiency, safety, and patient acceptance." "Demonstrated safety" was defined to mean "no serious toxicity (and few significant side effects) reported in 3 years' clinical use." This coincided with the theme of the October-November sales campaign, which was "Taking patients off MER/29 is bad medicine!"

In November seven major medical magazines carried advertisements for MER/29 which proclaimed that MER/29's "use in over 300,000 patients reaffirms the safety margins established in early laboratory and clinical data." It is interesting to note that when Merrell submitted this advertisement to the *Journal of the American Medical Association* they were requested to tone down their safety claims. The quoted sentence was changed to read that after MER/29's "use in more than 300,000 patients, few toxic or serious side effects have been reported, thus tending to reaffirm the safety margins previously established." Other changes were also made, and both advertisements are reprinted here for comparison.

after 3 years' clinical experience:
here is what we now know about MER/29 and .

Two-page advertisement which appeared in fourteen major medical journals from July to November 1961.

.;...what we are learning about atherosclerosis

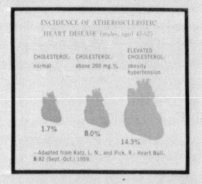

after 3 years' clinical experience:
here is what we now know about MER/29 and ...

WE KNOW HOW MER/29 ACTS

We know that MER/29 lowers cholesterol in as many as 8 out of 10 patients, even without dietary restrictions. In 576 patients studied by various physicians, average cholesterol levels dropped from 303 mg.% to 241 mg.% —an average decrease of 62 mg.%. We know that MER/29 reduces total sterols in both blood and tissue.

We know that MER/29 does this by inhibiting the body's own production of cholesterol.

We know that, after use in more than 300,000 patients, few toxic or serious side effects have been reported, thus tending to reaffirm the safety margins previously established.

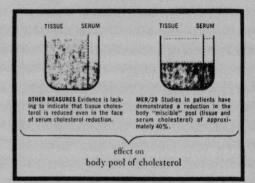

OTHER MEASURES Evidence is lacking to indicate that tissue cholesterol is reduced even in the face of serum cholesterol reduction.

MER/29 Studies in patients have demonstrated a reduction in the body "miscible" pool (tissue and serum cholesterol) of approximately 40%.

effect on
body pool of cholesterol

WE HAVE OBSERVED CONCURRENT BENEFITS

In some patients, concurrent clinical benefits have been reported to attend the use of MER/29. Published papers on MER/29 therapy to date report improvement in 50 of the 79 anginal patients reported in these studies, and comparable results are being obtained in similar studies now in progress. Among the other benefits reported are:

decreased incidence and severity of anginal attacks
improved ECG patterns
diminished nitroglycerin dependence
increased sense of well-being

"During triparanol [MER/29] therapy there was a definite improvement in the electrocardiographic tracings in response to exercise in 3 of 11 subjects with angina pectoris."
—*Hollander, W.,* et al.: *J.A.M.A.* 174:5 (Sept. 3) 1960.

"Nitroglycerin requirements decreased in 3 [of 5 out-patient] patients, including the patient showing electrocardiographic improvement....Three [of 4 private male patients], after a lapse of some weeks, showed improvement in exercise electrocardiograms, which was sustained but not further improved in subsequent observations."
—*Corcoran, A. C.,* et al.: *Progr. Cardiovasc. Dis.* 2:(Pt. 1) 576 (May) 1960.

"Of the 45 patients with coronary artery disease followed for 1 year, 16 had a history of frequent anginal attacks. Fourteen of these spontaneously stated that their angina disappeared within 2 months of [MER/29] therapy....In one patient...with persistent coronary insufficiency pattern (ST segment depressions in multiple leads), there was a complete reversion to a normal tracing during MER/29 therapy with associated clinical improvement in angina."
—*Lisan, P.: Progr. Cardiovasc. Dis.* 2:(Pt. 1) 618 (May) 1960.

Two-page advertisement which appeared in the Journal of the American Medical Association from July to November 1961.

...what we are learning about atherosclerosis

While the advertisements honestly stated that "no one can yet be certain" that lower cholesterol levels "will prevent or alter atherosclerosis," they did not mention hair loss, ichthyosis, or the increasing reports of eye trouble, which by that time had blossomed into several documented instances of cataract formation. On January 30, 1962, as part of Senator Kefauver's investigation of the drug industry, Dr. Arthur Sackler, the head of Merrell's advertising agency, was asked why all this was not mentioned. He contended he did not know about the cataracts at the time the advertisements were prepared. His flip attitude with regard to the hair problems is reflected in the following colloquy with Senator Roman Hruska (R., Neb.), one of the drug industry's chief apologists:

> *Senator Hruska:* Doctor, there was some learned debate here on the seriousness of thinning of the hair. Seriousness, after all, is a matter of relative nature. When people come to a physician to be treated for an excess of cholesterol and they seek thereby to see that they do not drop over dead in case cholesterol has anything to do with cases of heart failure, the thinning of hair would fade into relative insignificance, would it not, on a comparative or relative basis?
>
> *Dr. Sackler:* Senator, as a personal choice, I would prefer to have thin hair to thick coronaries.
>
> *Senator Kefauver:* What was that?
>
> *Dr. Sackler:* I said I would prefer to have thin hair to thick coronaries.

At this point a committee staff member commented, "I am sure you would, Dr. Sackler, except that your ad itself points out that there is yet no assurance that you will avoid thick coronaries by the use of MER/29." Indeed, two and a half months after Merrell filed MER/29's New Drug Application, Dr. McMaster had admitted to Dr. Ancel Keys that they could not claim that the drug was "actually capable of arresting or reversing atherosclerosis" in humans. Dr. Sackler's testimony before the Kefauver committee was nevertheless reported to Merrell's salesmen as an instance where "MER/29 was used as an example of a drug which may have a few side effects, but which is marketed because these possible side effects are *far* outweighed by its unique usefulness."

On the day after the October 26 meeting Dr. Nestor wrote a memorandum to his superior, Dr. Kessenich, recommending that since MER/29 "produces serious toxic effects in humans and since this drug has not been conclusively demonstrated to have any material clinical benefit, consideration should be given to immediate suspension of this NDA as the potential benefit is not warranted by the definite risk." Dr. Nestor emphasized that Merrell "knowingly has withheld pertinent information" from the Food and Drug Administration.

In the meantime Merrell had called Merck and asked their permission to submit a summary of their findings to the FDA naming Merck as the source. Merck agreed but requested an opportunity to review the summary before it was submitted. From the point of view of accuracy, it was lucky they did. There were many errors in Merrell's version, but perhaps the most serious was that they consistently referred to the eye changes in the rats as being "corneal" rather than as cataracts. As Dr. Peck, the head of Merck's toxicology-pathology department, noted in a memorandum to his superior, the changes they observed "were definitely lenticular." He further noted that "Dr. King, at the time of his meeting in our laboratories, did say that the ocular changes in the rats were different than those they had observed in their animals." This latter statement is interesting because, as we have seen, King told Dr. Van Maanen that the eye changes in the Merck rats "are similar to those observed in our group."

Dr. Peck's comments were forwarded to Merrell. Shortly thereafter Dr. Werner called Merck and asked them to prepare their own summary and submit it to the FDA, which Merck did. Later, on December 1, Dr. Werner would write Dr. Peck saying that he wanted him to know "that we really appreciate what you did" and that he wanted "to compliment you and your folks on the quality of work done." As a token

- 2 -

a) **Dog Study:** (continued)

    20 mg/kg/day (continued)

We examined these dogs after six months' administration of MER-29 and confirmed the haziness of the uvular structures. The two other dogs were normal. Of the two affected dogs, one was a male and the other a female.

10 mg/kg/day. The dogs tolerated the drug very well. After six months' administration of MER-29, no ocular pathology was observed. The staff of the outside laboratory considered some of the lenses of these dogs to be edematous.

We could not confirm this edematous observation.

b). **Rat Study:**

Groups of 25 male and 25 female rats received 10, 25, and 60 mg/kg/day of MER-29. The drug was suspended in carboxymethyl-cellulose and administered by gastric tube.

    60 mg/kg/day. After 7 weeks of drug administration, a corneal haze was noted in some of the animals. After administration of MER-29 for 3 months, 35 out of the 50 rats showed this corneal change.

    25 mg/kg/day. After administration of MER-29 for 12 weeks, some rats in this group showed a corneal haze. At the end of 3 months, 20 out of 50 rats showed a definite corneal haze.

    10 mg/kg/day. After 3 months' administration, none of the animals showed any ocular change.

After administration of MER-29 for 3 months, the drug treatment was stopped. The animals were further observed in order to determine whether regression of the corneal lesions occurred. No regression was observed 3 months after the drug was withheld. At the same time, those rats which did not show corneal changes remained normal.

The corneal changes observed by this outside laboratory in the rats are distinctly different from the eye changes observed in the dog. Even though we have observed these corneal changes in our laboratories, the incidence of this change is far higher in this particular study.

Dr. Peck's handwritten corrections on Merrell's report of Merck's animal studies.

of his "appreciation" Dr. Werner enclosed a check for $250 which he hoped would be used "any way you see fit." Dr. Peck returned the check saying, in effect, thanks but no thanks.

Merrell must have guessed what Dr. Nestor's reaction at the October 26 meeting had been, for president Frank Getman and vice-president Robert Woodward arranged to see his superior, Dr. Kessenich, on November 2. Dr. Nestor was not invited but as he testified later, he "felt that if the drug that I was working with and was such a hot potato was going to be discussed, I wanted to be there." He said he learned about the meeting "quite by accident" and "just walked in and sat down, and nobody threw me out. So I stayed."

In a memorandum written several days after the meeting, Getman described what happened: He recalled to Dr. Kessenich that Merrell had "voluntarily added 'thinning of the hair' as a side effect from the drug" and that they had tried to alert physicians to discontinue MER/29 therapy if their patients developed hair or skin changes, but that the warning letter had not yet been approved by the FDA. He told Kessenich that when Merrell learned of the Mayo cataracts they "felt an obligation to advise the medical profession immediately." Getman, amazed at what he thought was bureaucratic red tape, "wanted to know why we were unable to meet the obligation we felt to the public and the medical profession." Dr. Kessenich told him that the letter proposed "fundamental changes" in the MER/29 literature and needed FDA approval. Getman replied that the recommendations contained in the letter "seemed obvious" and that he saw no reason why the letter could not be sent out first, thereby warning the profession, and if the FDA had any changes they wished to have incorporated, they could be added in a supplemental letter. Dr. Kessenich refused this suggestion, Getman said, but assured him "that he would make a decision at the earliest possible date."

Woodward's recollection of the November 2 meeting was more bitter. He noted that Dr. Kessenich contended that drug companies should submit "any and all" information they might receive about a drug's toxicity at the time they received it without screening it for significance or reliability. Woodward recalled that it was apparently Kessenich's view that all questions of scientific judgment were "apparently reserved only for the FDA and that we are not entitled to render a judgment except in an accompanying evaluation to the report submitted."

When Nestor mentioned that he believed MER/29 should be withdrawn, Woodward told him that it was "the biggest and most important drug in Merrell history," having "done more for the reputation of the company" than any other product. "I further informed him," Woodward noted, "that if we decided that the inherent risk outweighed the efficacy, they (FDA) would not have to take action as we would do it first. He therefore knows that we are at this time confident of our product and its contribution and that, furthermore, we intend to defend it by every available means."

This "fight to the death" attitude expressed by vice-president Woodward was the subject of a November 9 memorandum from Getman to Richardson-Merrell's president, H. Robert Marschalk. Copies of the memorandum were sent to H. Smith Richardson, Jr., and other corporate officers. It was entitled "Voluntary Withdrawal of MER/29."

> As you know, our prime strategy with the FDA has been to agree upon a revised brochure coupled with a caution letter to physicians on side effects of the drug which have developed since widespread use following marketing. This continues to be our objective, and we are exerting every effort to achieve it.
>
> In thinking ahead, however, we have to consider our course of action in the event the FDA moves to legal action through seizures [of MER/29] or to administrative action through a hearing to suspend the NDA. Our attorney with the most experience in this field has suggested we give consideration to voluntary withdrawal.
>
> Attached is an analysis of the pros and cons of such

action. You may be able to think of others, and I would appreciate having them. In any event, now is the time we should weigh them carefully, as it is quite likely the final decision may have to be made on the spur of the moment —probably less than 24 hours.

The current established policy calls for an all-out fight whatever the action by the Government. This preparation has been made solely as a basis for re-evaluating that decision and determining whether we should change.

As far as Merrell is concerned, we remain completely satisfied that we are doing patients a tremendous amount of good with a very small amount of hazard for any patient taking the drug. The biggest hazard we face is the seriousness of an allegation of cataracts, and the seriousness which would be attached to the wide variety of side effects associated with the drug whether justified or unjustified.

The first clinician—Wm. Hollander, M.D., of Boston— who has had an opportunity to review all of the data (animal as well as human) in our files and in the hands of the FDA, feels that it would be a crime to remove the drug from the market—he feels that such removal would pose a threat to research progress in the United States and to the welfare of the people in our country. He has worked with the drug for more than three years and has observed no serious side effects. Aside from his own experience, he is familiar with the results physicians in his area are getting with the hundreds of patients they are treating. This is the first opinion we have from a recognized clinician who has been made familiar with all the data in the hands of the FDA.

I would appreciate your giving this your very early consideration as we are dealing with an unknown time factor.

Attached to the memorandum was Getman's summary of the various arguments. The first-listed reason for voluntary withdrawal was that "Merrell would take credit for removing the drug from the market rather than being forced to do it by Government action." Getman noted that if they fought the FDA and lost, "Merrell and Richardson-Merrell would be tarred with a reputation of attempting by every means to continue to sell a product which is dangerous to the health of the American public." He warned, however, that even if they won, Merrell's sales would fall and the ensuing bad publicity could also "be used as an example before Congressional committees of the necessity for more stringent laws and regulations to permit quicker action. . . . Voluntary withdrawal in cooperation with the FDA," on the other hand, "would probably put us in a somewhat better position for further negotiations in obtaining [approval for] NDA's or negotiating questions which arise on marketed products."

The arguments against withdrawing the drug were divided into two groups. The first centered on Merrell's contention that MER/29 was a worthwhile drug which adversely affected only a small number of people, estimated by Getman to be less than one-half of one percent. The second group of arguments were based on more practical business considerations. Getman pointed out that even if the Food and Drug Administration forced MER/29 from the market they could nevertheless "continue marketing the drug internationally, with appropriate warnings." This could not be done, however, if they voluntarily withdrew it from the United States market. Another consideration was the fear that "product liability claims will undoubtedly increase if we voluntarily withdraw because of side effects."

By brigading the arguments for and against withdrawal, the memorandum significantly reveals that Merrell recognized a serious, albeit unknown risk of continued marketing. Their decision to keep MER/29 on the market must be viewed in light of this realization. Specifically, Getman noted:

> As of the state of our knowledge today, the reported side effects are low numerically and serious side effects very few in number. Unlike Flexin and similar product withdrawals, we have had no deaths reported. We believe that discontinuance of the drug at the first sign of a rash or falling hair should preclude any danger of serious side effects. On the other hand, *this is unknown*. Changes in the eye occur months later—even months after discontinuance of the

drug. *If* these are drug induced, we have no way of knowing how many cases may develop in the next few months, nor of spotting them accurately in advance. Further definitive research to establish this point in humans is extremely difficult because of the very low incidence. At high doses in dogs and rats, we and others have found an effect on the eye— this would undoubtedly lead many scientists to conclude that the reported human instances are drug induced. If the number of serious side effects increases significantly, the drug should be withdrawn.

The memorandum is also significant because Getman reported that if the FDA tried to force MER/29 from the market, they would probably "allege that Merrell withheld important data and information," adding that "all information has been given to the FDA, but admittedly it was not done at the time it came to our attention."

On November 13, 1961, twelve FDA staff members, including Drs. Nestor and Kessenich, met to consider the future of MER/29. In a memorandum of that meeting, they noted that "considerable evidence has accumulated to cast considerable doubt on both the claimed efficacy and safety" of the drug. "Data indicate that the drug does not lower cholesterol to the degree claimed and many toxic reactions are resulting from the use of the drug in both experimental animals and humans. Much of this information did not become available to us until recently although the producer of the drug had it for several months." They then reviewed the FDA's reason for not immediately approving Merrell's warning letter:

On October 17, 1961, [*sic;* should probably read "October 18"] Dr. F. Joseph Murray of William S. Merrell Company phoned to inform us that the Company had learned a few days earlier that the drug was producing "lens changes" in humans. He wanted permission to put out what amounted to a very weak warning letter to physicians. We requested complete information about the toxic reactions to evaluate before agreeing to this. As this information was gradually made available to us over the next three weeks it became obvious that the Company had been withholding from us significant information about adverse toxic reactions in both animals and humans. This necessitated considerable delay in order to evaluate the newly presented data and to search for more that might not have been made available.

The withheld evidence of which the memorandum here speaks, and to which Getman referred in his memorandum, was the studies conducted by various clinical investigators and animal experimentors indicating that MER/29 might not be as safe as Merrell contended. The FDA did not yet know the details of the Merck study, nor did they know of the discrepancies between what Merrell did report to them and what was actually observed in the company's laboratories.

After appraising the information known to them at the time, the FDA staffers agreed on the following:

> (1) The drug should be removed from the market and the application suspended.
> (2) The firm should be requested to cooperate to this end.
> (3) If the firm does not cooperate, a strong warning letter to physicians should issue immediately, and a notice of hearing to suspend the NDA should issue.

Accordingly, shortly after the meeting, one of the participants, Dr. Ralph Smith, chief of the New Drug Branch, called Merrell and asked them to voluntarily withdraw MER/29 from the market. The firm refused and requested another meeting. It was scheduled for November 16 (or 17, there is some dispute).

If the November 2 meeting was designed as an informal exchange of ideas giving each side an opportunity to sense the other's position, the one hold on November 16 (or 17) was a full-scale confrontation. In addition to Getman and Drs. Werner, Bunde, and McMaster, Merrell was represented by the parent company's general counsel as well as by Bradshaw Mintener, a Washington lawyer who since his stint as

Assistant Secretary of Health, Education and Welfare in the Eisenhower Administration had made a career out of representing companies before the Food and Drug Administration. The head of the FDA's contingent, which included Drs. Smith and Nestor, was Deputy Commissioner John Harvey.

The Merrell representatives repeated their contention that MER/29 was a valuable drug and therefore should be allowed to remain on the market. They emphasized that they had wanted to warn the medical profession to discontinue MER/29 therapy if the patient developed hair or skin changes and wondered why the FDA had so far refused to agree to this. The FDA reiterated that Merrell's warning letter was weak and that in any event the drug should be withdrawn.

At the end of the meeting Harvey promised to discuss the next step with his staff and to call Getman later in the day with the FDA's decision. He would subsequently explain that although almost everyone agreed that MER/29 "should be removed from the market" (he later admitted that the drug "should not have gone on the market in the first place") they did not feel that there was sufficient legal basis to force a recall or formally to suspend the effectiveness of the New Drug Application. The FDA's only recourse was to require Merrell "to issue a warning letter."

In testimony before Senator Hubert H. Humphrey's subcommittee Dr. Nestor would later charge that "non-medical men, including laymen, have been making medical decisions," and he cited the MER/29 case as an example. FDA Commissioner George Larrick "categorically" denied Nestor's charges and contended that as of November 1961 the evidence in support of suspending MER/29's New Drug Application was "inconclusive." Senator Humphrey came to Dr. Nestor's defense and, in a prepared statement dated March 21, 1963, affirmed that in his view the "documents in the subcommittee's possession would appear to confirm that the clinical evidence in the New Drug Application was definitely insufficient to establish safety (or efficacy) of the drug before it was cleared in the first place."

After discussing the MER/29 problem with his staff, Deputy Commissioner Harvey called Frank Getman and advised him that the FDA had decided against trying to force the drug off the market but would require that a comprehensive warning letter be mailed to the medical profession. A meeting was arranged for November 21 to draft a suitable document.

The Merrell group (which included Getman and Drs. Bunde, Werner, and McMaster) attended the November 21 meeting prepared for a give-and-take session but were instead presented with a *fait accompli*. As Dr. Bunde wrote the following day, the FDA contingent arrived with Ozalid copies of a letter, "still damp and barely legible." Merrell was told, according to Bunde, "that this was the letter [the FDA] worked hard to put together and we were expected to take it as is with no essential change." He described how he and his colleagues read the letter "in silence," trying not to show their "shock." Dr. Bunde commented, however, that he thought they "were aware of it."

Merrell's strongest objection was the letter's suggestion that every patient taking MER/29 undergo a special eye examination using a microscopic device called a slit lamp. This machine projects a narrow beam of light into the eye and illuminates the lens, allowing the ophthalmologist to examine it under high magnification, and is useful in detecting early cataracts. Merrell argued that a slit-lamp examination would prove too expensive for the patient, with the practical result of discouraging physicians from prescribing MER/29. Furthermore, they pointed out, the slit-lamp examination was not necessary because cataract formation was always preceded by severe skin and hair changes and that the drug could be discontinued if these developed. The FDA was not dissuaded, however, and the reference to the slit-lamp examination was retained. Dr. Bunde concluded his memorandum by noting his "very strong impression that these people [FDA] do not consider this drug toxic but consider it useless and are only taking this toxicity thing as a means of getting us off the market according to the law, which is confined to safety."

On November 24 Merrell received another report of a patient who developed cataracts after taking MER/29. This was the fifth. A further meeting with the FDA was held on November 27, and on December 1, 1961, Merrell sent the following letter to the 232,361 physicians and osteopaths in the nation:

Dear Doctor:

In cooperation with the United States Food and Drug Administration, we are writing to inform and caution you concerning adverse effects, including some unpublished reports, associated with the use of MER/29 (triparanol). Although comparatively few serious clinical injuries have been reported to date, their possible significance is emphasized by findings from animal studies.

Cataracts. Four cases of cataracts in humans are reported in patients who have received MER/29. One of these cases occurred in a patient receiving the recommended dosage of 250 mg. of MER/29 daily.* Cataracts and corneal opacities have also been produced with MER/29 in animals. Slit lamp examinations are necessary for early detection of developing cataracts. For this reason such examinations are indicated prior to and periodically during therapy. Before this problem came to our attention, approximately one thousand persons being treated with MER/29 were patients of ophthalmologists. Most of them have had careful eye examinations, including use of the slit lamp, before and during drug therapy. Results on these patients will be reported to you as soon as they are available.

---

* The fifth patient to develop cataracts, which Merrell learned about on November 24, was also taking MER/29 at the recommended dosage of 250 mg. per day. Despite the fact that Merrell met with the FDA on November 27, the agency was not informed of this fifth patient until after the warning letter had been sent. When Dr. McMaster was asked at one of the trials why he did not just pick up the telephone and call Dr. Nestor to report the fifth cataract case, he replied he "could have, but this would not have been the custom."

Hair changes. There have been many cases of hair loss, either baldness or thinning hair, changes in hair color and texture, and loss of body hair. Such hair changes may be related to the skin changes discussed below as well as to the eye changes described above. It is recommended that MER/29 therapy be discontinued promptly at the first evidence of hair or skin changes to minimize progressive effects possibly including eye injury.

Ichthyosis and other skin changes. There are reports of skin reaction ranging from dryness, itching, and scaling to severe exfoliation [shedding], and ichthyosis. Some of these changes were also associated with hair loss and cataracts. It is recommended that MER/29 therapy be stopped immediately if such skin changes occur.

Depression of Adrenocortical Function. Adrenocortical function depression as shown by reduced output of adrenal steroids has been produced by MER/29 in animals, and in man at high dosage levels. This effect has not been ruled out in humans at recommended dosage levels. Appropriate precautions should be observed if MER/29 is employed in patients with suspected borderline adrenocortical function or in patients who are subjected to stress.

Other Adverse Effects. Other clinical effects reported include four possible cases of leukopenia [decreased production of white blood cells] and scattered cases of abnormal liver function tests, impotence, diminished libido, vaginal smear alterations, nausea, vomiting and urine test changes simulating proteinuria [excretion of protein in the urine]. At a level of 25mg/kg per day of MER/29 deaths have occurred in some dogs within 35 days, with liver damage in some animals. It has caused abortion and prevented conception in rodents, diminished spermatogenesis in dogs, stopped egg laying in chickens, and was assumed to cause acute intravascular hemolytic [destruction of red blood cells] episodes in some dogs in one study.

The side effects of all types reported to us to date total substantially less than one percent of the patients treated. This includes a number of patients who have been treated with MER/29 in clinical research studies for continuous periods of more than a year, including a few in excess of three years.

In view of all reports concerning adverse effects, it is

recommended that MER/29 be used only in patients who can be maintained under very close supervision and frequent observation. Dosage should never exceed 250 mg. per day.

Further studies are under way to assess more fully the incidence and seriousness of adverse effects, with a view to a re-evaluation of the conditions and indications for use of MER/29. We will appreciate any information you may contribute from your clinical experience with MER/29.

Sincerely,

CARL A. BUNDE, Ph.D., M.D.
Director of Medical Research

Concurrently with the mailing of the warning letter, Richardson-Merrell issued a press release—which, however, did not mention the specific side effects. President Marschalk explained this to his top corporate officials by stating that the company did not "want to endanger its relations with the doctors by 'practicing medicine in the newspapers.'" In other words, Merrell did not want stories associating MER/29 with cataracts to frighten potential customers. Accordingly, they were concerned when both *Newsweek* and *Time* made inquiries concerning the warning letter.

In a reply dated December 12 to *Time*'s Cincinnati correspondent, the chief of Merrell's professional relations department, Dr. John B. Chewning, outlined Merrell's position. The letter emphasized that while there were a few cataract cases, "substantially" less than one percent of those who had taken the drug had any side effects at all. Dr. Chewning reported that "*no definite conclusion* has been reached that the side effects are positively due to the drug" and noted that the company was compiling case histories on approximately one thousand patients who had been undergoing eye examinations while they were on MER/29. He asked the *Time* correspondent to delay the story at least until the results of the survey were available, arguing that revealing the contents of the warning letter to the public would only cause panic and would "take the application of medical judgment away from the physician."

Newsweek contacted Merrell through their medical writer, Matt Clark. Inasmuch as the warning letter was signed by Dr. Bunde, Clark called him. Dr. Bunde answered a few questions, and later Dr. Chewning called Clark to further explain the company's position. The following is a transcript of their conversation, which was introduced into evidence at one of the trials.

> *Clark*: You people have been doing animal studies, haven't you?
>
> *Chewning*: We have been doing animal studies, but I don't have access to the data.
>
> *Clark*: You don't have any idea what percentage of animals developed cataracts?
>
> *Chewning*: No.
>
> *Clark*: O.K., then we'll just say that "cataracts" have occurred in a *certain proportion.*
>
> *Chewning*: We might say *eye changes;* we don't know these changes in the animal are the same as in the human.
>
> *Clark*: What animals are these?
>
> *Chewning*: Again, I'm not sure. You see I'm not in research and I don't know exactly which animals are used. Eye changes have been observed—but, and this is what complicates it: dosage response levels, duration the drug is administered, and under what conditions.
>
> *Clark*: I realize that. I point out that at least two of the patients have exceeded the recommended dosage.
>
> *Chewning*: Where did you get this?
>
> *Clark*: This was according to Dr. Bunde, and he said possibly three had taken more than recommended. *The Washington Post* said that at least one had been known to follow the recommended dosage. I think that's a little unfair. I'm making the story as short as possible. I'm putting into story that eye observation is currently underway. I think it is very interesting and important.

On December 14 Dr. Chewning reported on these developments to Frank Getman. The memorandum reveals the extent to which the company tried to avoid unfavorable publicity.

> On Monday, December 11, we received a telephone call from the Cincinnati *Time* correspondent. It was a routine

investigation about MER/29, traceable to the UPI story [about the warning letter]. We replied with a letter answering the questions. It was delivered personally and amplified. The story was filed after 5 p.m. on Tuesday.

You were informed of the first contact and we agreed upon the strategy and you had an opportunity to approve the letter.

Our next move was to follow up with the medical editor, Mr. Gilbert Cant, on December 13. However, the report was that Cant was ill and out of the office.

I presented to [Merrell vice-president] Bob Woodward a recommendation that we retain Harold Mantell. He is an old friend of Gilbert Cant and has worked with us before on MER/29 during the preparation for the Princeton Conference in 1959. I thought that Mantell would be best qualified to approach a man like Cant to learn exactly what his editorial decision would be.

The problem was then complicated by two developments: 1) *Newsweek* picked up the UPI wire and started preparing a story for their next issue; 2) a Washington *Time* correspondent called Kloepfer at PMA [the Pharmaceutical Manufacturer's Association—a drug-industry trade association] to ask for a copy of the Beasley testimony before the Kefauver subcommittee. He learned that they were trying to associate the need for revision of the Food and Drug laws with the MER/29 warning letter. It was an attempt to build a case that this would not have happened if we had the laws that Senator Kefauver wants us to have.

Kloepfer replied correctly that legal compulsion was not necessary in this instance and that the company had acted responsively and voluntarily. He defined the question of efficacy for the correspondent.

We were prepared to offer Cant an expanded cholesterol story, but with these developments, we thought it best to first kill the Kefauver–MER/29 association and, if possible, to use the *Newsweek* story to kill a *Time* article. We could expect better treatment in *Newsweek* than we could from the sharp-worded *Time*.

Mr. Mantell talked with Cant. The most probable result is that *Time* will not carry an MER/29 story in the next issue. Cant may accept our letter offer to give a full report on the patients now under observation by ophthalmologists.

It should be understood that this is not his final decision, but probably reflects his editorial judgment not to hit us with a story this week but wait for the product make-or-break story in January.

Time did not run a story on the warning letter, and Merrell did get "better treatment" from *Newsweek*. The story, headlined "Worth the Risk," contained the statement: "If MER/29 reduces heart attacks [failing to mention that this had not been demonstrated], it is worth the risk of cataracts." At around the same time, and in dour counterpoint to the *Newsweek* story, the British government, which had previously rated MER/29 as having "not been proved of therapeutic value," asked Richardson-Merrell to voluntarily remove the drug from the market. The company refused.

As we have seen, Merrell did not have to clear communications to its clinical investigators with the FDA. Accordingly, on November 29 letters were mailed to them over Dr. McMaster's signature, with a copy of the warning letter enclosed. The covering letter explained that the "overall incidence of reported side effects from MER/29 remains gratifyingly low" and that Merrell was "certain that their existence need not interfere with your further use of the drug."

Dr. Steinberg, the physician with the National Heart Institute who had reported on the accumulation of desmosterol in MER/29-treated patients, objected to this optimistic interpretation of what he felt was a very serious situation. In a letter to Dr. McMaster, he pointed out that since there was "no assurance" that drugs which lower cholesterol levels actually benefit the patient, "the acceptable incidence of toxic effects must be as near to zero as possible." As this was not true with MER/29, he argued that "it is not justifiable to expose the patient to potentially damaging effects."

Dr. McMaster, in a letter dated December 28, 1961, responded that he appreciated Dr. Steinberg's views but that they were "not shared by those of us who have access to the greater bulk of data and reports concerning the drug or by an impressive number of other experts in this field. Furthermore I believe any attempt to deprive the fully informed practicing physician of his right to exercise professional judgment in the selection of treatment for any particular patient is not consistent with the accepted philosophy of medical practice in the United States."

This latter comment by Dr. McMaster is of special interest because on October 31, 1961, when Merrell already knew about four cataract cases, he wrote the following to a physician who had reported that two of his patients on MER/29 therapy were complaining of "black spots before their eyes":

> This is so unusual a report that I would like to ask you to provide us with additional details about these patients. In fact, we have never before heard of anything remotely resembling this. It would be important, for example, to know whether ophthalmologic examination has revealed anything of interest which may help to explain this phenomenon. It would also be important to learn whether these "black spots" are fixed or floating and whether the patients have experienced anything of this sort previous to MER/29 therapy. Also, have either or both of them had any other possible side reactions—for example, dermatologic involvement? This would be important inasmuch as the eye and skin are both of ectodermal origin.

Not one word about cataracts, although the information he sought clearly reveals that this is what he had in mind. When asked about it at one of the trials, Dr. McMaster demurely replied that he did not know "in specific dealing with [the physician] whether we should alert him to the fact that we had reports of cataracts, but most certainly the symptoms he reported to our salesman had nothing to do with cataracts, and for this reason I think the reply and the query that I made of [the physician] in this instance was well taken." When the attorney for the injured plaintiff read from a standard medical text that "in the incipient stage [of cataract development] the patient may complain of seeing

spots which occupy a fixed position in the field," * Dr. Mc-
Master replied that he did not agree.

Nor was Dr. McMaster alone at this late date in preferring not to tell inquiring physicians that MER/29 might cause
cataracts. On November 21, 1961 (the very day that Merrell
and the FDA were discussing the form of the warning letter), Dr. Chewning wrote to a physician that MER/29 "appears to be remarkably free of serious side effects," noting,
however, that "there are conditions like thinning or falling
of the hair which have been reported." Although he advised
the physician that the drug should be discontinued "at the
first sign of these effects," Dr. Chewning did not mention that
cataracts might result if it were not.

Merrell was similarly less than candid with their salesmen. On November 8 the men were instructed: "Return all
—all—MER/29 materials to the home office immediately."
They were not told why—merely that "a major promotional
revision" was being considered in conjunction with a supplemental New Drug Application which had been filed with
the FDA. A week later they were directed to recite the following set speech whenever a physician asked for a sample
of MER/29: "Doctor, I'm temporarily out of complementary
stock, but I'll be glad to have some sent from Cincinnati."
They were to "avoid such statements as 'They called all my
samples in,'" as it "will only lead to misunderstanding and
rumor."

On December 1, concurrently with the mailing of the
warning letter to the physicians, a copy was sent to Merrell's
salesmen. They were told not to be alarmed by the "rather
lengthy list of side effects" and to remember that "it has not
yet been *definitely* concluded that the 4 cases [there were, of
course, by that time five] of eye changes are drug related."
Two weeks later the company wrote to pharmacists stating
that despite all the adverse publicity, MER/29 was still being

---

* May's *Diseases of the Eye*, p. 264 (22d ed., 1957). See also Kirby,
Surgery of Cataract, p. 138 (1950).

prescribed by "physicians throughout the country." The letter urged them "to make sure that your stocks of this high-volume specialty are adequate."

Merrell recognized that the warning letter would cut deeply into sales. A week before the final FDA-approved version was mailed, Dr. Bunde noted gloomily in a confidential memorandum to Getman that the company would have to change their promotional tack if they were to maintain their sales volume. Fretting that any advertising "literature, any handouts, any exhibit material which must make the full disclosure that we will be stuck with will do more harm than good," he suggested circumventing the FDA restrictions by "getting the true story told at medical meetings and publications" by physicians, who are not subject to the FDA restrictions. He recommended that a team be set up to collaborate with the physicians and that they "make an all-out effort to get as many doctors talking at meetings, small and large, and presenting papers in journals, important and unimportant, as can possibly be attained."

It does not appear that this blitzkrieg ever progressed beyond the planning stage. Neither did Dr. Chewning's suggestions of what to do if MER/29 were to be forced from the market. One was a unique plan to have Merrell institute a "Cēpacol-bottle-a-month plan" (Cēpacol is another Merrell product) to reimburse those patients who returned their unused supply of MER/29. He also wanted the company to *"accumulate all letters* from patients who state that they must have the drug or that they are willing to assume the risk for continued benefits of the medication." These expressions of patient support could be used, he suggested, to "build a ground swell of public demand" to have the drug restored to the market.

Before MER/29's last three and a half months, from January until April 12, 1962, are examined, one other unbelievable occurrence should be mentioned. It can only be explained charitably as incredible carelessness. A chronology prepared by the Mayo Clinic for a Senate investigating committee, recounting Mayo's experiences with one group of patients on MER/29 therapy, has the following entry under November 6, 1961:

> The drug company [Merrell] representative called inquiring if we had further information as to side effects of MER/29. We had nothing new. The drug company representative mentioned that some dogs on MER/29 had been rechecked. Those animals on supplemental vitamins and minerals had developed no skin or eye changes, while some of those on no supplemental vitamins or minerals had developed these complications. He suggested supplemental vitamins and minerals for our patients with cataracts.

On the same day Dr. McMaster, according to his memorandum of November 7 to Dr. Bunde, "related the story of the dogs who were protected by multiple vitamin and mineral supplement plus Vitamin E" to another clinical investigator.

Apparently, the only experiments in which animals were given MER/29 in conjunction with a dietary supplement were the rat and dog experiments running from April, 1961, to the end of that year. As we have seen,* by the middle of November 1961, 100 percent of the female rats and 70 percent of the male rats given MER/29 plus vitamins and cholesterol developed what Merrell termed eye "opacities," and those receiving the dietary supplement developed the "opacities at a faster rate than those who were on the drug alone. Furthermore, all of Merrell's seven surviving dogs developed cataracts whether they were given the dietary supplement or not. Representatives of Merrell have been unable to point to an experiment, other than those just described, which might have been the basis for what Dr. McMaster, and the unnamed "company representative" referred to in the Mayo chronology, told the physicians.

The December 1, 1961, warning letter prompted additional reports of suspected cataracts, and Merrell undertook an

* See chart on page 83.

extensive survey in an attempt to determine if MER/29 was the actual cause. On January 19 *The Medical Letter,* which had previously recommended that MER/29 "be reserved for experimental trial," warned its subscribers that the drug "should not be used at all." By February 23, 1962, Merrell knew of seventy-one cataract cases.

Despite the warning letter, Allen Toole was not taken off MER/29 until January 1962.° By that time, he later testified, things had gotten so bad that he could pluck the hair off his arms and his skin was "very flaky and scaly." He told how he "could rub my arm like this and it would just peel off in little pieces." His wife "used to complain about having to wipe it up off the chairs and around the house."

Toole testified that these conditions lasted until March 1962, when they gradually began to clear. He thought he was probably getting better, and was relieved. He did not realize that MER/29 had already given him cataracts—which would take several more months to develop. In April, however, he read an article about MER/29 and "was quite startled because it described all of my symptoms to the exact T, and then at the end it said something about cataracts, which sort of gave me a jolt." By June his vision was "a little foggy." It was as if he were bound and gagged, hopelessly watching the sparkling fire eat the fuse on its way to the bomb which would make him blind.

In November he underwent surgery to have the opaque lens in one eye removed. Two months later they operated on the other eye. For the rest of his life Allen Toole would have to wear large and cumbersome eye glasses or special contact lenses, or he would be blind.

In March 1962 Merrell resumed advertising MER/29. An advertisement in the March and April issues of the *American*

° Few physicians keep good records showing which of their patients are taking what drugs. A prominent New York products liability lawyer who tried several MER/29 cases took MER/29 even after it had been withdrawn from the market because his physician had failed to contact him. Fortunately, he suffered no apparent ill effects.

CURRENT CONCEPTS OF ATHEROSCLEROTIC HEART DISEASE

the coronary-prone patient can be identified

MER/29
triparanol

- inhibits cholesterol synthesis
- lowers body cholesterol
- lowers total body sterols

> Nota Bene: In prescribing MER/29, review descriptive literature in full.

A significant advance in combatting heart disease, our number one medical problem today, is the possibility of identifying patients who may be "coronary risks." This can now be done "many years before any overt symptoms or signs become manifest," on the basis of the latest findings of the Framingham study, Dawber and Kannel state.*

So far, three "easily determinable" coronary risk factors have been "clearly demonstrated" by this study, begun in 1949. When cholesterol levels above 250 mg.%, or hypertension, or left ventricular hypertrophy was present at the beginning of the study, the incidence of atherosclerotic heart disease eight years later was 50% higher than average. A combination of two or three of these factors increased the incidence up to fourfold.

The predictive value of cholesterol levels is indicated by these findings:

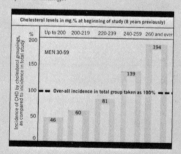

On the basis of these findings, Dawber and Kannel make this strong recommendation:

"It has seldom been possible in noninfectious diseases to identify such highly susceptible individuals years before the development of disease. The physician should be aware of his ability to do so, and should recognize the challenge it imposes...which demands a primarily preventive rather than therapeutic approach."

The Wm. S. Merrell Company
Division of Richardson-Merrell Inc.
Cincinnati, Ohio / Weston, Ontario

Merrell
SINCE 1828

*Dawber, T. R., and Kannel, W. B.: Mod. Concepts Cardiovasc. Dis. 30:671 (July) 1961.

Advertisement which appeared in seven major medical journals in March and April 1962, including the April 16 issue of Modern Medicine.

Heart Journal, the *American Journal of Cardiology, Annals of Internal Medicine, Circulation, M.D. Medical News Magazine, Medical Economics,* and *Modern Medicine* trumpeted MER/29's value in reducing cholesterol levels. While it did not boast of the drug's safety, as had previous advertisements, neither did it specifically mention the side effects. Rather, a small box in the advertisement carried these words: "Nota Bene: In prescribing MER/29 review descriptive literature in full." Similarly, a promotional piece distributed directly to physicians merely warned them to discontinue MER/29 if either hair or skin changes developed. Again, no mention of cataracts.

At around this time Merrell and the FDA were locked in a bitter dispute over proper wording for the new MER/29 literature. We have already seen that as early as August 2, 1961, Merrell had wanted to amend its brochure to recommend that MER/29 be discontinued at the first sign of hair or skin problems. On October 26 they submitted a revised brochure, which cautioned:

> While MER/29 is usually well tolerated at a dose of 250 mg. daily, there have been a number of reports of hair thinning, changes in color or texture of hair and dermatitis. More recently lens opacities have been rarely observed following severe dermatitis. This has only occurred when drug therapy has continued for a period after the dermatitis appeared. Therefore your patient should be informed to report any hair or skin changes to you and MER/29 should be immediately withdrawn if changes in hair and skin occur.

This revision, together with Merrell's draft of a warning letter similarly submitted on October 26, was rejected by the FDA as being inadequate.

Merrell tried again on December 22. This time the package insert advised the physician that "cataracts have been reported in a small number of patients who have received MER/29" and warned that it should be discontinued after the first signs that the drug may be affecting the skin or hair. Furthermore, the physician was advised, "periodic slit lamp examinations provide the best means for early detection of any developing cataracts." Merrell also mentioned that cataracts were observed in dogs after four to five months on MER/29 at dosages of 20 to 40 mg. of the drug per day.

This too was deemed unsatisfactory, and on March 16, 1962, Merrell submitted yet another draft, together with the detailed results of their cataract investigation. Briefly, it noted that the incidence of cataracts among MER/29 patients was comparable to that of the general population and that the types of cataracts which were observed did "not reveal a consistent pattern of cataract formation which would be expected" if they were being caused by a drug. Nevertheless, the Merrell draft warned that "MER/29 therapy should be promptly discontinued at the first evidence of any drug reaction" and that "the recommended dose should not be exceeded."

Merrell's statistical survey of cataract formation and causation, according to Getman's testimony, supported the "unanimous opinion" of the company's medical and scientific staff that a causal connection between MER/29 and the cataracts "had not been established." This was not the view of the Food and Drug Administration. On April 3 the FDA's Bureau of Program Planning and Appraisal told Dr. Nestor that on the basis of their review of the ophthalmological reports "the incidence of cataracts in MER/29 patients is extremely high."

At the end of March, Dr. McMaster received a letter from Dr. Achor at the Mayo Clinic informing him of another cataract case, a six-year-old boy. The boy had been suffering from severe familial high cholesterol, and many different remedies had been tried without success. (His brother had also been afflicted with extremely high cholesterol levels and died from coronary atherosclerosis at the age of seven.) In August 1960 he had been given MER/29 at a dose of 250 mg. a day, in addition to various other cholesterol-lowering agents, and had showed some improvement. A year later, in August 1961, his physician noticed that his skin was dry and that his hair was turning a lighter color. By October he had developed ichthyosis. At that point MER/29 was reduced from one capsule a day to one every other day. In November a slit-lamp examination failed to turn up any opacity in the lens. In March 1962 he was given another slit-lamp examination and incipient cataracts were discovered in addition to crystalline deposits in his corneas. Dr. Achor noted sadly that it appeared "that this case represents another of the ectodermal reactions to [MER/29] therapy" and that this was "unfortunate since of all possible cases where [cholesterol-lowering] therapy is needed, this patient has the most urgent indication for it."

On April 2, 1962, Drs. Bunde and McMaster flew to Rochester, Minnesota, to check first hand on the condition of the boy. When they returned Dr. McMaster wrote that it was "hard to explain" two of Dr. Achor's cases (presumably including this six-year-old) "by anything unrelated to [MER/29]." He reported that Dr. Achor "said he would not again use [MER/29] even in a high risk patient, unless all other agents and procedures failed." This memorandum was written on Friday, April 6, 1962; on Monday morning the FDA would arrive at the gates and demand to see the toxicology laboratory records. Three days after that, Merrell would inform the FDA that it wished to withdraw MER/29 from the market.

Merrell president Frank Getman testified that the decision to withdraw MER/29 had been made on Friday, April 6, *before* the FDA discovered the discrepancies in the animal toxicology data. The decision was made, he said, at a top-level staff meeting of himself; Edmund R. Beckwith (who was to succeed Getman as president of Merrell); Robert H. Woodward, a Merrell vice-president; and their chief scientist, Dr. Werner. The primary reason for abandoning their "wonder drug," at least in Getman's mind, was that the FDA had put them in an "untenable position with the practicing physician on the information we could give him about the drug." By this he meant that Merrell and the FDA were unable to agree on the content of MER/29 literature and that the company felt unduly restrained in its promotional activities because of it. Merrell scientists did not believe MER/29 caused the observed cataracts, Getman asserted, but they could not disprove causation and therefore the FDA insisted that it be acknowledged in their literature. What made it especially difficult, he testified, was that his company's proposals were "being reviewed by a physician who personally did not believe in the cholesterol theory" of atherosclerosis.

Although Getman testified that Woodward kept notes of the meeting, they could not be found in the course of the subsequent investigations. This is significant, because Merrell's claim that their decision to call it quits with respect to MER/29 was an internally motivated decision, unrelated to the FDA's discoveries on April 9 and 10, is contradicted by several contemporary events. First, Dr. Nestor and his entourage from the FDA were never informed of the decision while they were at Merrell's plant examining the animal records. Second, Dr. Murray's memorandum of April 11, quoted earlier at some length, assumes that MER/29 was still a viable product which had to be protected. (It is possible, of course, that he had not yet been informed of the decision.) Third, and this is most crucial, a memorandum dictated by Getman on the morning of the FDA visit strongly indicates that the decision to abandon MER/29 had not yet been made. The memorandum was dated April 9 and was directed to, among others, H. Smith Richardson, Jr., who was by that time Richardson-Merrell's chairman of the board, and H. Robert Marschalk, Richardson-Merrell's president. Marked confidential, the memo explained that "Recent developments have made it imperative that we have a top level review of our proper approach to the *continued marketing of MER/29* as soon as possible" (emphasis added). The date selected for this important meeting was Thursday, April 26. Getman then noted, in a beautiful example of ironic foreshadowing, that "at the time of dictating this memo, Dr. Nestor, Dr. Goldenthal—an FDA pharmacologist—and a local FDA inspector are at Merrell getting full information on all developments to date."

The April 26 meeting never took place, for three days after Getman foresaw the need to reevaluate their plans for the "continued marketing of MER/29," the FDA was notified that Merrell was withdrawing the drug. A week later, on April 17, Getman wrote to the nation's physicians that the drug was being withdrawn because of "additional reports of side effects of the kind reported" in the December 1, 1961, warning letter. Getman promised that Merrell would continue to have "an extensive research program in cardiovascular disease," pointing out that "MER/29 has been one important phase in this effort" and that their experience with the drug "has made contributions to basic knowledge in this field." *
This must have been small comfort indeed to those patients with MER/29-induced cataracts as they waited for surgery to restore their sight.

---

* The letter as originally drafted by Merrell stated that the drug was being withdrawn because "continuing research and clinical experience has raised some questions concerning the possibility of an unacceptable incidence of side effects" but that this "experience has not established that MER/29 is unsafe when used as recommended." It explained that the decision to withdraw the drug was being made "out of an abundance of caution" and that it would remain off the market "until all possible controversy is put to rest." Although the FDA found this draft "unsatisfactory" and insisted that it be rewritten, this was the draft which was released to the press and which was used in explaining Merrell's action to the public.

6

The Selling of MER/29

"[This] was advertising written not for you or for
me or someone to read in the subway cars; this
was directed only to physicians because they had
to prescribe the drug. Even though they took what
may be more than literary license, it was directed
to a scientific audience and an audience which
should be capable of reading between the lines." *

On Saturday April 14, 1962, Philip Ritter III, the Merrell vice-
president in charge of promotion, sent a memorandum to each
of the company's salesmen explaining that MER/29 was being
voluntarily withdrawn from the market. They were directed
to tell any inquiring physicians: "While we do not believe that
there is any causal relationship between MER/29 and serious
side effects such as cataracts, nevertheless, Merrell desires to
protect you (the doctor) and your patients from that possibility and that accordingly we are voluntarily withdrawing
the drug."

From that point on, while cataract-stricken patients lined
up to sue for their injuries and Merrell was being investigated
by not only the federal grand jury in Washington but by three
congressional committees as well, Merrell's salesmen turned
their attention to other products. Behind them were twenty-
two months of hard work which helped to make MER/29,
in the words of the 1961 Richardson-Merrell annual report,
"the most successful drug in Merrell's 133-year history."

* Former United States district court judge and former Deputy Attorney
General Lawrence E. Walsh defending Richardson-Merrell in *Roginsky* v.
Richardson-Merrell, February 8, 1966.

Merrell had promoted MER/29 as it had never promoted a drug before. Between June 1960 and April 16, 1962, forty-five different advertisements were placed in thirty different medical journals for a total of 380 times. Over 160,000 physicians received a looseleaf binder delivered by Western Union and some fifty-nine pieces of literature, each mailed separately. Merrell's postal bill attributable to the MER/29 promotion for the thirteen months from June 1960 through June 1961 was estimated at over $140,000. Selected physicians, hospitals, and medical schools received a nine-minute sound film which similarly advertised MER/29. For the fourteen-month period beginning with May 1960, MER/29's advertising and promotion budget was estimated at over $1.5 million, 23 percent of the projected sales for that period. Merrell's total promotion and advertising budget for the fiscal year 1960–61 was just under $8 million—28 percent of its $28 million total sales. In contrast, their research expenditures (so often pointed to as justifying what many believe to be exorbitant drug prices) for the same period was a mere $1.7 million—6.2 percent of sales.

As extensive as all the journal and direct-mail advertising was, the great bulk of promotion was done by the man in the field: the drug company salesman, or detailman, as he is called. Journal advertising and direct-mail may lay the groundwork by making the physician generally aware that a certain drug exists, but it is the detailman, in face-to-face promotion, who often has the most influence on what a physician will prescribe. A 1958 survey of physicians by the American Medical Association indicated that 68 percent considered the detailmen their primary source of information about drugs and relied heavily upon their advice in deciding what to prescribe. Despite this heavy responsibility, the detailman is not scientifically trained; he is a salesman, not a medical man.

Merrell, like many pharmaceutical concerns, provided its salesmen with selling presentations, called structured details, which the salesmen were to memorize and perform for the

From the desk of
Frank N. Getman
The Wm. S. Merrell Co.

[handwritten note:]

MER 29

Advertising Promotion Budget

Through June 1960

751,263

Fiscal 60-61 858,872

Total 1,610,135

074801

Getman's recapitulation of MER/29's advertising and promotion budget for the period May 1960 to July 1961.

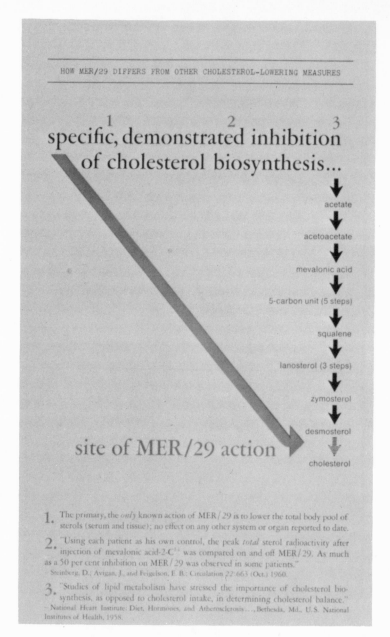

Two-page advertisement which appeared in eighteen major medical journals in April, May, and June 1961.

...leading to specific, demonstrated advantages in cholesterol-lowering therapy

particularly in patients with coronary artery disease, generalized atherosclerosis, and other conditions thought to be associated with abnormal cholesterol metabolism

MER/29 REDUCES CHOLESTEROL IN AS MANY AS 8 OUT OF 10 PATIENTS: MER/29 reduces both serum and tissue cholesterol without strict adherence to diet. Although some physicians prefer to use MER/29 in conjunction with controlled diets, cholesterol can be reduced successfully without such limitation.

CONCURRENT BENEFITS REPORTED IN SOME PATIENTS: In patients with coronary artery disease, some of the concurrent benefits reported include decreased incidence and severity of anginal attacks, improved ECG patterns, diminished nitroglycerin dependence, and increased sense of well-being.

MER/29 HAS PRODUCED FEW SIDE EFFECTS, NO TOXICITY: Patients have been treated with MER/29 for continuous periods up to 19 months. In no case has there been evidence of serious toxic effects on the function of any vital organ or system. Side effects (nausea, headache, dermatitis) are rare and have usually been associated with dosages greater than those recommended for effective therapy.

MER/29 is compatible with other cardiovascular therapies. It can be used along with measures which control anxiety, hypertension, obesity and other conditions associated with cardiovascular disorders. These include nitroglycerin, PETN, and anticoagulants.

CAUTION: Since long-term MER/29 therapy may be necessary, periodic examinations, including liver function tests, are desirable. Also, since MER/29 inhibits cholesterol biosynthesis, and cholesterol plays an important role in the development of the fetus, the drug is *contraindicated in pregnancy.*

DOSAGE: One 250 mg. capsule daily, before breakfast.

SUPPLIED: Bottles of 30 pearl gray capsules.
Complete bibliography and product information available on request.

The Wm. S. Merrell Company
Division of Richardson-Merrell Inc.
Cincinnati, Ohio • Weston, Ontario.   Trademark: MER/29

physician. The kits came complete with visual aids, which in the case of MER/29 included a tube of cholesterol and a grisly color photograph of a horribly clogged artery, and were psychologically designed to overcome any resistance a physician might have. Like the journal and direct-mail advertising, the structured details of the MER/29 campaign emphasized the drug's benefits and either ignored or glossed over its shortcomings. Rarely were MER/29's serious side effects ever mentioned.

In June 1961—after Merrell had learned of one suspected human cataract case, had seen cataracts in two of its dogs and in all of the Merck dogs and rats, and had concluded that MER/29 was causing hair color changes and hair loss—an advertisement in eighteen major medical journals proudly stated that "side effects (nausea, headache, dermatitis) are rare" and that "in no case has there been evidence of serious toxic effects on the function of any vital organ or system." In November, after Mayo reported its two human cataract cases and after Merrell's rerun of the Merck study produced cataracts in its dogs and "opacities" in the eyes of its rats, advertisements appeared in seven major medical journals proclaiming that MER/29's "use in over 300,000 patients reaffirms the safety margins established in early laboratory and clinical data." In March and April 1962, the last two months of MER/29's life, advertisements in medical journals merely noted that physicians should "review descriptive literature in full."

Nor was Merrell alone in preferring not to give physicians the whole truth about a drug in their promotional material. A survey conducted in 1959 by the Library of Congress indicated that some 89 percent of drug advertisements appearing in medical journals did not disclose the complete side-effect risk. Clearly, the industry was proceeding on the premise that keeping the physician uninformed was the best way to sell its wares. This is in stark contrast to the Principles of Ethical Drug Promotion adopted by the Pharmaceutical Manufacturers Association, which provide that "prompt, complete, conservative and accurate information concerning therapeutic agents shall be made available to the medical profession."

Merrell began its pre-marketing campaigns for MER/29 before it was even certain that its New Drug Application would be approved. We have already seen how in 1959 Merrell attempted to get military hospitals to study MER/29 not for "honest clinical work" but as "pre-marketing softening prior to the introduction of the product." They tried this tactic again in February 1960, when they dispatched forty-four of their top-flight salesmen throughout the country to introduce MER/29 to the nation's leading cardiologists and internists. By March 14 this special elite force reported that 81 percent of the 457 physicians they contacted agreed to try MER/29 on their patients, even though the drug had not been approved by the FDA and was available for experimental purposes only.

The regular detail force was told that this pre-marketing softening of the medical opinion-makers would make their task that much simpler once the drug was released. However, they were warned not to jump the gun, because it was *"still* premature to discuss the product with your physicians." Rather, they were directed to memorize the following set speech and repeat it whenever a physician inquired about the drug: "MER/29 is a very significant drug, from all that I have heard. However, I do not have complete information on the drug and it is not available for sale as yet. Rather than risk misleading you on such an important medical advance, I would rather reserve any comment until I can discuss MER/29 thoroughly and with authority."

Apparently any physician who persisted in trying to learn something about MER/29 (several clinical investigators had already published papers in medical journals on the drug) was met with a blank stare, for the detailmen were admonished that MER/29 was a "once-in-a-lifetime opportunity" which was not to be jeopardized "by being premature." They were told to "*stick* to the instructions you have received—for *your* best interest; for your company's best interest!"

In preparation for their "once-in-a-lifetime opportunity" the detailmen were given instructions on how to best utilize their selling efforts in the crucial period when MER/29 would first be available. So that they would not waste their time speaking to physicians whom the company felt were not worth detailing, the salesmen were told to score all the physicians in their territory using a specially devised "Physician Call Plan." Each physician was to be ranked and placed in one of three categories. The first group, considered "the 'cream of the crop' in every respect," were to be detailed most often. They were the physicians who not only had a large practice but also wrote many prescriptions each day and were very influential with their colleagues. The ideal "cream of the crop" M.D. was also young—for as Merrell explained it, the older the physician the fewer were his "years of prescription potential." It made no sense to thoroughly detail a physician today and have him drop dead tomorrow.

The second group comprised those physicians who were deemed "average or above average in most respects." These M.D.s did not have as large a practice, did not write as many prescriptions and were not as influential as those in the first group, and would accordingly be detailed less often.

Since the purpose of the Physician Call Plan was to select those M.D.s who "offer the greatest potential for MER/29" and to "eliminate 'dead wood'" from the detailman's territory, those physicians who had small practices, wrote few prescriptions, and were not very influential were placed in the third category. They were considered to be "of little value to Merrell," and were therefore detailed only a few times a year.

With the battle plan thus carefully mapped and the key objectives identified, the detailmen waited until Merrell headquarters indicated that they should start promoting MER/29. Once they received the go-ahead, they fanned out into the field armed with their memorized structured details and visual aids. Although during MER/29's twenty-two-month life the detail was changed several times, its basic pitch was the same: MER/29 safely and effectively lowers cholesterol levels and reduces the severity of heart-disease symptoms for some patients. The first version began: "Doctor Brown, let us talk about people who have atherosclerosis. Any issue of the A.M.A. *Journal* will indicate how serious this disease can be . . ." At this point the salesman was directed to take the current issue of the *Journal of the American Medical Association* and turn to the obituary section, where he had previously circled the names of those M.D.s who died from atherosclerosis.

After this somber reminder that death is universal the physician was presumably ready to be sold on the virtues of Merrell's new wonder drug. He was told that various studies indicated a three to six times greater risk of heart attack in persons with abnormally high cholesterol—and that MER/29 reduced the amount of cholesterol in the blood to safe levels. While noting that this was MER/29's "primary action," the detailman assured the physician that there were also "many clinical reports of MER/29 helping some very sick people feel very much better." After reviewing a few supporting case histories, the detailman concluded his presentation:

> "Doctor, all these cases illustrate that MER/29 reduces cholesterol significantly and that in some patients very important improvements in health have occurred.
>
> "Just one capsule daily is the dosage."
>
> *Option 1* (if MER/29 is stocked in his hospital):
> "MER/29 is available everywhere including your hospital, doctor, for your hospitalized patients."
>
> *Option 2* (if MER/29 is not stocked in his hospital):
> "MER/29 can be made available for your cardiac patients in your hospital, doctor, if requests that it be stocked are made by a number of doctors. If you write your request on your prescription pad, I'll be glad to drop it off at the hospital for you."

"Doctor, the fact that over 75% of America's board cardiologists have prescribed MER/29 says perhaps more than I can say about the efficacy and safety of the drug. I am confident you will want to provide your post-coronary and coronary-prone patients with the benefits and protection afforded by MER/29. Is there any reason why you won't prescribe MER/29 in patients where high cholesterol is implicated?"

If the physician complained that MER/29 might be too expensive the detailman had a ready response: "It is the least expensive and most effective cholesterol-lowering drug that has ever been offered, doctor. It should cost your patients somewhere in the vicinity of only 33 cents a day." He did not mention, and most likely did not know, that one MER/29 capsule, for which the patient had to pay 33 cents, cost only 6.5 cents to produce. The wholesale price to the druggist was just under 20 cents.

Probably because of the high price of drugs many physicians expect pharmaceutical companies to be extremely generous in giving them free samples. Merrell, however, wanted to sell MER/29, not give it away. The detailmen were told not to be overly liberal with their limited supply of samples, since "MER/29 will become long-term therapy" and it will be "difficult to refuse a doctor once you have him started." They were to give free bottles of MER/29 to only their "most important physicians" and only if the doctor refused to prescribe unless he was given a personal supply. If asked for a sample by anyone else, the detailman was directed to say: "I'm sorry, doctor, we are not sampling MER/29. (Pause; this may satisfy him.) Since it will be a matter of weeks for MER/29 to demonstrate its full effect, sample quantities are impractical."

Merrell was not content merely to promote MER/29 to the physician through the detailmen and medical-journal advertising; they also promoted the drug to the pharmacist with the hope of influencing the physician indirectly. Since pharmacists are not permitted to recommend prescription drugs, Merrell's promotional effort was ostensibly merely to make them aware of the drug's existence. This was Ritter's testimony: "The pharmacist is an important member, in our view, of the health team. . . . It is important that pharmacists know about the drugs that their doctors are writing. Many, many times a pharmacist will catch an error in a prescription. If he has knowledge of the drug he will call the doctor and question any error that has been made. It becomes important to keep him informed even though he cannot influence the sale in any respect."

The final sentence of Ritter's statement is interesting because the January 9, 1961, issue of his newsletter for the detailmen, *$ales Talk*, proudly reported that a detailman "makes sure every pharmacist knows the pertinent facts about MER/29 . . . *plus* the important point that MER/29 is not stealing sales from any other product on his shelf." He "tells the pharmacist to discuss and sell MER/29 to his doctors, and the prescriptions will mean all *new* business." Earlier, advertisements run in several druggist-oriented journals had advised the pharmacist that since "MER/29 is long-term therapy" each "prescription means continual refills."

Merrell also wanted to have the laboratories which ran cholesterol tests for physicans to push MER/29. The September 22, 1960, issue of *$ales Talk* reprinted this report from one of their detailmen, presumably to suggest this lucrative source of business to the rest of the sales force: "I found out today that the biggest lab in Washington D.C. sends back the following note on the test sheet returned with the patient's cholesterol determination: 'We recommend MER/29 for reduction of cholesterol.' Not bad for a lab that does 80% of the tests in town."

In addition to directly influencing the physician through journal advertising and face-to-face selling, as well as indirectly through the pharmacists and laboratories, Merrell also wanted to ensure that the drug's ultimate consumer—the pa-

announcing... MER/29
triparanol

the first cholesterol-lowering agent to inhibit formation of excess cholesterol within the body, reducing both serum and tissue cholesterol levels.

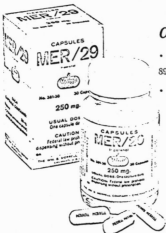

advantages:

• MER/29 reduces circulating cholesterol in 86 to 89% of patients, with or without dietary restrictions.

• MER/29 directly inhibits cholesterol biosynthesis.

Stock up ... on unique **MER/29** *... one of the biggest prescription products in 1960.*

PRICE ℞ MER/29	SUGGESTED	
	LIST	WHOLESALE
381-30 Bottle of 30	$9.84	$5.90

THE WM. S. MERRELL COMPANY
NEW YORK • CINCINNATI • ST. THOMAS, ONTARIO

Promotional literature directed to pharmacists.

tient—would also know how valuable it was. A wonder-drug-conscious public, used to and expecting instant cures, would bring added pressure on the reluctant physician to prescribe MER/29.

While Merrell would later defend not listing the drug's side effects in the press release announcing the mailing of the December 1, 1961, warning letter on the ground that they did not want to antagonize physicians by "practicing medicine in the newspapers," this same restraint was not apparent when the company wanted to promote the drug. On June 9, 1960, Dr. Chewning wrote an extensive memorandum to Merrell president Getman reviewing their plans to publicize MER/29 in the lay press. Not only were stories given to major newspapers, science reporting services, and the national wire services, but all of the major popular magazines were also approached.

Most magazines, it appeared, were not too anxious to rush into print with the MER/29 story. Dr. Chewning reported that the *Reader's Digest* wanted "more clinical evidence before they will do a story." The medical editor of *Parade* magazine was "opposed to any story on the product" because, Chewning explained, he belongs to "a small group of science writers who do not believe in the cholesterol-lowering approach [to the treatment of atherosclerosis and heart disease]."

At *Coronet*, Getman was told, "Walter Ross is tough, and is not about ready to take the story. Our approach will be through a free-lance writer who has already been selected." There was a "fairly good chance of a short report" in *Cosmopolitan*, Chewning wrote, and they were trying to interest *Redbook* in a story with "the angle of 'How to Keep Husbands Alive'."

While he was hopeful of being able to plant MER/29 stories in some of the magazines, Dr. Chewning noted that a good many of the medical editors were wary of the subject: "We find that the press is a sensitive indicator, and from the responsible medical editors we get questions which are not unlike those being asked by physicians. The story has not been completely sold, and some editors are still waiting for more clinical confirmation." These "responsible medical editors" were evidently more careful in approving drug stories for their magazines than the Food and Drug Administration was in approving drugs for the public.

One of the magazines which did run a piece on MER/29 was *Time*, although Dr. Chewning complained that *Time*'s medical editor, Gilbert Cant, had given it a "semi-negative twist" by raising the specter of desmosterol. Nevertheless, Merrell played this story up to the hilt in a special "extra" issue of *$ales Talk: "Time* waits for no one—MER/29 is no exception. The 'Medicine' section of the latest issue praises MER/29 in an article: 'Cutting the Cholesterol.' This issue will be in the hands of over 3 million persons. Publicity of this kind will send thousands of patients to their doctors asking about MER/29. Make sure they walk out of the offices with prescriptions."

The June 17, 1960, issue of *Medical World News* also covered MER/29, but apparently not to Merrell's liking. They quoted Dr. Corday (who was to later report the first cataract case to Merrell) as saying that he "stopped using MER/29 after trying it on 75 patients" because he felt it was too toxic. Dr. Corday made the statement during a symposium on various cholesterol-lowering agents at an American Medical Association meeting. However, *Medical World News* also reported that other panelists did not agree with Corday's evaluation of MER/29. In the course of their clinical experience with MER/29, they found the drug to be an effective cholesterol-lowering agent "with only minimal toxicity." One of these panelists was Dr. Philip Lisan of the Hahnemann Hospital in Philadelphia. In the "Letters to the Editor" section of the July 15, 1960, issue of *Medical World News*, Dr. Lisan complained that the magazine had given a distorted picture of the symposium and pointed out that, contrary to the impression conveyed, MER/29 was a safe drug.

A copy of Dr. Lisan's letter appears in Merrell's files with the following notation across the top: "To be given to Philip Lisan, M.D. as suggested letter to *Medical World News*. R. H. McMaster, M.D." Dr. McMaster later testified that it is common practice for pharmaceutical companies to write scientific papers for physicians because often they lack writing ability or the library facilities to properly report on their work and that he saw nothing wrong in the reports being "ghostwritten" by the manufacturers of the product being evaluated. With respect to Dr. Lisan's letter, he said that he did not remember whether Lisan had asked Merrell to draft it or whether he had first approached Lisan with the idea. In any event, on August 15, 1960, a copy of the letter was forwarded by Merrell to the FDA. On the bottom of the copy was a handwritten note, evidently from Dr. Lisan to Dr. McMaster: "Bob—Here is a copy of the letter I sent to-day air mail. P.L." There was nothing to indicate to the FDA that it was written by Merrell and not Dr. Lisan.

On July 12, 1960, Merrell's sales force received a revised "considerably strengthened detail . . . with ample ammunition for second round detailing of doctors already on MER/29." The detail, which again emphasized that MER/29 was a safe cholesterol-lowering agent and that it also alleviated some heart-disease symptoms in patients with "normal cholesterol levels," had new closing paragraphs designed to "overcome any tendency to wait and see on the part of any physician":

> "I hope you'll agree that there are perhaps ten patients in your practice who fit into one of these categories who deserve the help that your prescription for MER/29 will provide.
> "The only way you'll ever satisfy yourself about the value of this significant drug is to pick such patients out and prescribe one capsule of MER/29 for them daily, as soon as possible."

This directive was criticized by Getman in a July 27 memorandum to Ritter entitled "Let's Start Selling." He was concerned that MER/29's sales were not meeting expectations and wanted Ritter to "take a close, critical look at the way we are stimulating the field force on MER/29."

> Very frankly, [Getman wrote] I have seen almost nothing going out of here in the way of good sales promotion ideas. The last revision of the detail was not very outstanding in my regard. It still seems pretty complicated for the GP [general practitioner], with a lot of long terms where shorter words would work. This is one that we discussed, and I find that no change was made in the closing which asked to put 10 patients on it. Why 10? To me it makes sense to ask a doctor to try a drug on two, three, or possibly five patients, but if we're going above that, why not ask for all of them? What do you think of a closing that says in effect, "I'm sure that you will want to place all of your postcoronary and coronary-prone patients on MER/29."

Getman's criticism apparently prompted the abandonment of plans to merely supplement the revised detail in August. In a memorandum dated July 29 the sales force was promised that by September 1 they would receive "an all new Detail Aid that will strengthen considerably your presentation of the startling facts about MER/29."

A September 1960 issue of *$ales Talk* reported proudly how one divisional sales manager was stimulating his men to sell their physicians on MER/29's benefits. It reads a little like Knute Rockne was supposed to sound in his famous pep talks to his Notre Dame team:

> *Bristol Inspires His Division*
> Yes, if you're in a leading division on MER/29, watch out for Joe Bristol's boys. They were fortunate enough to hear one of the finest presentations about how to sell MER/29 we have heard yet. Joe's personal touch helps, but his message is loud and clear even in print:
>
> Gentlemen, we have witnessed the most successful launching of a new product in the history of the Merrell Company—in the introduction of MER/29!!!!
>
> This introduction was made by 300 sales representatives

using a STRUCTURED DETAIL—one that was FIELD PROVEN before release to you.

With this STRUCTURED DETAIL, and through the inevitable process of constant practice, the successful MER/29 salesman has learned his sales story far beyond the "canned" stage. He is able to deliver his message to the doctor in a completely personalized manner. His delivery is a tone of enthusiastic personal conversation—a conversation built on the formula of logic and reason, picturing the doctor's patient enjoying the benefits of using MER/29. A canned sales story???? Well, some might call it that, but the successful MER/29 salesman *knows it* past the canned stage. IT IS A DYNAMIC, MOTIVATING DETAIL DESIGNED TO INFLUENCE THE DOCTOR TO PRESCRIBE MER/29!!!

Enthusiasm is just as contagious as the small pox!! It is the spark that makes the sales flame into a reality. It is the fuel on which a top sales representative operates. It is either high octane, medium octane, or basic mineral not yet refined. It is like electricity passing from the salesman to the doctor.

More men have become good salesmen just through enthusiasm than by any other method. If you believe in your product—if you become excited about MER/29—and start calling on doctors—your sales start to materialize!! Why? Because you are enthusiastic!! YOU should be enthusiastic about MER/29. Never before—and perhaps never again—will you get a product like MER/29.—YOU HAVE NO REASON NOT TO BE ENTHUSIASTIC—YOU HAVE NO REASON TO GIVE A "TONGUE IN THE CHEEK" DETAIL ON MER/29. YOU HAVE A PRODUCT THAT MOST OF YOUR COMPETITORS WOULD REALLY LIKE TO HAVE!!! YOU OWE IT TO YOURSELF—TO YOUR COMPANY—TO THE MILLIONS OF PEOPLE WHO NEED MER/29, TO BE ENTHUSIASTIC!!!

We are all enthusiastic—some more than others—over any new product. We detail the doctor—showing our enthusiasm, and he catches our "germ" of enthusiasm and prescribes our product. But somehow, after we've told our story over and over again, what happens? We forget to become enthusiastic!!! Our battery runs down. We need a recharge. Your company is just as good now as when you went to work for it—in fact, much better. You have better products—you have better opportunities—everything is better!!! You haven't sold ALL your doctors on MER/29—so how can you afford to let your enthusiasm die!!!

If MER/29 is worth discussing with a doctor on the basis of what it will do for his patients, then it is worth getting excited about. The basis of all selling is the ability to transfer your enthusiasm for your particular product or idea to your prospect!!! DEVELOP THIS ABILITY AND WATCH YOUR MER/29 SALES GROW!!! How do you develop this infective enthusiasm? EASY!! First of all, "brighten up" as you tell the doctor what MER/29 will do at the beginning of your presentation!!! Lean forward—toward the doctor—. Automatically tighten your stomach muscles as you make your presentation. This forces a change of the inflection of your voice and paves the way for deeper penetration of the benefits you are describing.

You may say—this is false enthusiasm!!! NEVER!!! NOT IF YOU BELIEVE THAT MER/29 will bring desired results to the doctor's patient!!!

Sales tools, portfolios, manuals, samples and other visual and tangible tools are made (1) to help guide your presentation —(2) to help guide the doctor's thinking—(3) to dramatize and point out important points—BUT UNLESS YOU USE THEM WITH ENTHUSIASM—they are very ineffective. THE COMPANY CAN FURNISH ALL THE TOOLS—BUT THEY CANNOT SUPPLY YOU WITH ENTHUSIASM. SHOW MORE ENTHUSIASM—AND SEE IT RE-FLECTED IN YOUR BONUS CHECK!!!

Evidently the "tightened stomach muscle"-enhanced enthusiasm was paying off. An August 2, 1960, "extra" of *$ales Talk* reported:

Remember that first month after Tenuate [a Merrell hunger-suppressing drug] was released? Phones were jammed, order desks were hopping, your wholesalers were calling you to report they were out of stock—again—and they needed more . . . by yesterday! Doctors only needed a few days to see that Tenuate really did all we said it did.

The introduction month for MER/29, June, was even *more* exciting than when Tenuate was released—today there's no question that doctors are getting far better results with MER/29 than we even suggested they would. Here are a few examples of enthusiastic medical acceptance of an important new drug:

The top-ranking official of a leading cardiology society just reported that he routinely puts all patients with cholesterol levels over 300 mg.% on MER/29. He's sending his encouraging findings to Cincinnati.

*   *   *

Several doctors have reported that they don't bother checking cholesterol levels of patients on MER/29. They know the cholesterol must be reduced—their patients tell them they feel better and can do more and more work.

The raft of lay publicity continues on and on.

Almost every green slip that is sent to the sales force includes an order for MER/29. Quantities are changing from 1/6 doz., to 4 doz., 30 per order . . .

*   *   *

But remember, this is only coming from hard work and an excellent selling job. As we learned right at the start, MER/29 does not sell itself. Every man must do more than just detail the product . . . he has to sell it.

On August 5 Getman, in contrast with his pessimistic memorandum to Ritter a week earlier, wrote the field force that while sales were booming they had "only scratched the surface of the potential of MER/29." Although "millions of patients can benefit from MER/29," it was being taken by "only thousands." "The challenge is yours," he concluded. "I am confident you will meet it. Each of us in Cincinnati is pledged to assist you in every way possible." This was Merrell's ultimate goal: lifetime, once-a-day therapy for millions of people. Thus, a July 1961 issue of *$ales Talk* proudly reported how one detailman "recently sold MER/29 for 17 top executives (*regardless of their present heart conditions*)" (emphasis added).

The enormous pot of gold was just below the horizon; Merrell could already see its reflected glow. And they kept the pressure on. *Campaign Strategy*, another Merrell publication aimed at the sales force, reiterated that "MER/29 has an *attainable* potential sale greater than all other Merrell products combined." This goal could be met, they were told, if they intensified their detailing efforts to get a mere one-third of the physicians in their territory to prescribe MER/29 for one new patient each week. If this were done, their "territorial sales should average over $73,000 in the first 24 months." At the end of the two years, if one-third of the 160,000 or so practicing physicians placed 104 new patients on MER/29 (one a week for two years), over 5.5 million people would be taking the drug every morning. Merrell's annual sales for MER/29 would then be around $400 million. In contrast, the consolidated sales for Merrell's parent corporation, Richardson-Merrell, for fiscal year 1960–61 were only slightly over $150 million (including Merrell's $28 million).

Merrell similarly wanted to expand MER/29's hospital sales. The detailmen were told that "*only half* of our *direct* hospital accounts have purchased MER/29 and that "*a majority of the 7,000 U.S. hospitals have not yet bought their first bottle.*" They were directed to do something about it:

> Select your *three* best potential *general* hospitals that have *not* yet stocked MER/29, and promise yourself that before October 7th they'll each be dispensing MER/29.
>
> Next, select three hospitals that *have* stocked MER/29 and promise yourself that their *September purchases will be at least double their July purchases.*
>
> Your detail should emphasize starting the coronary patient on MER/29 as soon as possible while he is still *in the*

hospital to be certain that he gets the added protection that only MER/29 can give.

Need we say more . . . go get 'em!

Merrell also had its salesmen approach young physicians who had just graduated from medical school. In August 1960 the detailmen were reminded that since hospital residents and interns "represent considerable future growth to all of us," they were to be especially cultivated. "The resident or intern who knows Merrell well and Merrell products is the prescribing physician who in the near future will be our most valued Merrell writer [of prescriptions]." To "break the ice," the detailmen were to give them free tie tacks bearing the caduceus medical symbol in addition to the regular spiel on MER/29.

Despite all the selling effort, MER/29's sales during its first six months on the market were below Merrell's expectations. Many physicians, some of whom were most likely heeding *The Medical Letter's* warning that the drug "should still be reserved for experimental trial," were reluctant to prescribe MER/29 until more was known. Merrell wanted to break their resistance. Accordingly, 1961 started out with a new campaign designed "to persuade 'wait and see' G.P.s and internists to prescribe MER/29 now for at least three patients." The detailmen were told: "It is no longer possible for you to 'wait out' undecided doctors. The time for very definite, forceful action is now. Such action is far and away your major responsibility this campaign." The "key" to creating a "desire to prescribe" was that "sick patients feel better" on MER/29:

> By now you can identify the doctors not using MER/29. Yet, you know they should be. Very often, you know most of the reasons for not using it . . . cholesterol may not be atherogenic, desmosterol is a question mark, possible liver toxicity, doesn't work, doesn't do anything fast enough, costs too much, Doctor "X" hasn't started it yet. *Are any of these legitimate? No! From our viewpoint: we know they aren't true, we know what MER/29 can do for a person who*

needs it, and we know they have not stopped top MER/29 salesmen. There is no point in trying to overcome each of these objections. That's the long way around.

The quick way to get the non-prescriber using MER/29 is to use every resource you have at your command to show him that he will be benefitting himself and his sick patients in a giant way just as soon as he uses MER/29. That's the doctor's hot button . . . and you *must* come down on it harder than ever before.

Yes, MER/29 works by lowering cholesterol . . . doctors know this. Now, show them they don't understand well enough yet . . . just how much MER/29 can benefit their patients!"

The keystone of this campaign, like the others before it, was the structured detail. The salesmen were directed to follow it *"word for word!"* because "it represents the present ultimate in positive presentation of our basic MER/29 claims." They were to practice it until it became a part of their "selling personality." The detail again emphasized that MER/29 effectively lowers cholesterol and helps "sick people feel better while they are getting better." Because there was "no longer any valid question as to its safety or lack of significant side effects," MER/29 could thus be recommended for "routine use." After reviewing case histories in which patients reported subjective feelings of well-being ("As many as you can . . . until he gets restless in his chair!!!"), the detailman concluded his presentation:

"With such encouraging results a part of the background of MER/29, we feel it warrants personal evaluation by every physician who sees such patients. As you know, because of the nature of this drug, samples have not been generally available. But, because many physicians have expressed a desire to evaluate MER/29 in their own practices, with their own patients, Merrell has provided a limited supply of the drug just for that purpose.

"I have been authorized to select a few outstanding physicians in my area to participate in an informal evaluation of MER/29. I would like to offer you the opportunity to par-

ticipate in this study, because I'm confident the results you
see will prove extremely valuable to you and your patients.

"Select five patients from your practice with a recent history of some manifestation of atherosclerosis. As part of the
therapy for these patients, initiate MER/29 one capsule daily
for a minimum of two to three months. Be patient and have
confidence in MER/29, and suggest to the patient that he
cannot expect immediate improvement.

"Then, after three months, judge MER/29 on the basis
of the improvement your patients report to you. If you will
do that, I'm confident you'll become one of the biggest users
of MER/29 in this area—to the benefit of yourself and
your patients.

"If you will participate, Merrell will send you the necessary materials for your study . . . and if nothing further
develops from it, at least you will have run your own series
of studies on MER/29 and reached a conclusion as to its value
to you. I would like to forward your name to our Professional
Services Department today, doctor. May I?"

This was the crux of Merrell's strategy—to persuade the
physician to test MER/29 on several of his patients at Merrell's expense and get him in the habit of using the drug in
his practice. The detailmen were warned, however, that the
clinical trial program was designed to "give an extra push to
your good G.P.'s and internists *who have not yet written their
first Rx for MER/29*" and that they were not to try it on just
any physician. It was to be used only on the "good prescriber
with a large practice" who indicated that he was waiting until
MER/29 was "evaluated properly." If the detailman felt that
the M.D. was "at the point of prescribing without being offered the study," they were "not to give him the chance to
put off his decision for another three months!"

The year 1961 not only brought with it the new selling
campaign to "use MER/29 clinical trials to push 'wait and see'
G.P.s"; it also brought increasing reports of serious side effects.
Nevertheless, Merrell continued to emphasize that MER/29
was perfectly safe. In June its salesmen were reassuring
physicians that, the FDA-approved warning in its literature to

the contrary notwithstanding,* "MER/29 is a safe drug for long-term use." When confronted with an alleged MER/29-induced side effect, the detailman was told to blame it on another drug which the patient might be taking, "even if you know your drug can cause the side effect mentioned."

As late as August, Merrell salesmen were instructed to boast that "MER/29 has demonstrated its safety . . . no serious toxicity and few side effects in over 3 years' clinical use and in over 400,000 patients." In October, after Merrell already knew of three cataract cases, its salesmen were warning M.D.s that "once a patient is on MER/29 he must stay on MER/29" and that "taking patients off MER/29 is bad medicine." When the September issue of *McCall's* reported that MER/29, once "thought to be entirely without side effects," was now found to cause some people to lose their hair and develop severe skin conditions. Merrell's detailmen were told how to "twist" the article into "a positive sales aid" by emphasizing that the side effects were infrequent and were "completely reversible" when MER/29 was discontinued. Cataracts, of course, are not reversible and were not mentioned.

Finally, on November 8, a month after they had learned of the two Mayo cataract cases in addition to the one reported by Dr. Corday in February, Merrell told its salesmen to stop detailing MER/29. They were directed to return all MER/29 material to the home office immediately and, instead of being informed that MER/29 might be causing cataracts, they were merely told that a "supplemental application for MER/29 has been filed with FDA" and that "a major promotional revision" was being considered. In December they learned the truth and were sent a copy of the warning letter. They were cautioned not to be alarmed at the "rather lengthy list of side effects," because "MER/29 benefits *in the overwhelming majority of patients* far outweigh the side effects reported in a relatively few patients."

* The caution statement in the MER/29 brochure read: "The long-term or lifetime effects are unknown."

On December 7 the sales force received an "interim detail" which was "to be memorized *word for word.*" It repeated the substance of the warning letter, but emphasized that "*all* of the side effects reported to us have a combined incidence of substantially less than 1%" and that the majority of patients on MER/29 "will continue to get the benefits of its cholesterol-lowering effect without incident."

By February 1962 Merrell's advertising department evidently saw the need for something new. The December 1, 1961, warning letter had severely curtailed MER/29 prescriptions, not to mention hurting the morale of the detailmen, and the company was still unable to reach an agreement with the Food and Drug Administration as to what they could say about the drug. It was therefore decided that the simple approach should be used. We have already seen how, beginning in March 1962, Merrell placed low-key advertisements which, while not warning of MER/29's side effects, did advise physicians to "review descriptive literature in full." They would follow the same tack in their direct promotion to the doctors. The detailmen were directed:

> Think over what we've told doctors about MER/29 during the past six months. To name just a few items, we have covered: MER/29 effectiveness, ways to identify coronary "risk" patients, the dangers of cholesterol, reported side effects from MER/29, etc., etc. In short, we have discussed a very wide range of topics with each doctor.
>
> This campaign, our objective is to bring together much of the information now available in a concise plan of action for the physician.
>
> The idea: Give information to the physician in the most useful form for him.
>
> By consolidating all the data we have discussed during the past six months, in a simple four-step plan, we can "clean [*sic*] the air" for many doctors, giving them a "set" course of action to follow in their practice.

The four simple steps recommended to the physician were: (1) that he should "request routine cholesterol tests" for his patients, to discover which ones have high levels; (2) that he should prescribe MER/29 for those patients found to have high cholesterol levels; (3) that he should discontinue the drug if hair or skin problems developed (the detailman was directed to "put side effects in proper perspective by making sure he understood that *all* side effects reported total less than 1% of patients treated"); and (4) that he should never prescribe more than the recommended dose of one capsule daily.

The structured detail, which outlined the four steps for the physician, was described as "designed to help the doctor develop a very clear understanding of the steps he should take in using MER/29. Through this technique, it is expected that many doctors will increase their use of the drug. Like human beings in general, the physician likes to have his actions spelled out for him. It gives him a feeling of confidence and permits him to act more freely." The detailmen were told that by "presenting physicians with this logical sequence of steps, you give them a firm course of action to follow." To assist the physician to "act freely," he was to be given an "MER/29 desk reminder" which contained a supply of laboratory request slips and was inscribed with the MER/29 imprint. The detailmen were directed to "introduce the pad during the fifth paragraph of your detail when you say 'By checking the block marked serum cholesterol every time you request laboratory work . . .'" At this point, the detailmen were told, "Make an actual check-mark in the serum cholesterol block on the first page. It will leave a lasting impression with the doctor of exactly what you are talking about."

This final detail sent to the sales force emphasized that MER/29 remained a "rational approach" to keeping cholesterol levels low, and this was Merrell's contention to the end. Merrell's press release announcing the drug's withdrawal quoted from the letter which the FDA would not permit the company to mail and claimed that "experience has not established that MER/29 is unsafe when used as recommended" but that the company's decision to stop selling it was based on "an abundance of caution." As late as February 10, 1964, Frank Getman, who by that time had been promoted to executive vice-president of Richardson-Merrell, stated that to the best of his knowledge no "causal connection has as yet been established" between MER/29 and the "side effects reported." Nevertheless, the Food and Drug Administration's May 22, 1962, order formally suspending the effectiveness of MER/29's New Drug Application declared that "clinical experience shows that MER/29 (triparonol) capsules are unsafe for use. . . ."

7

Reckoning

"After we got down in the jury room we just all looked at each other and all came out with the same remarks, that this company must be punished." *

As a result of its "no contest" plea to the federal grand jury indictment, Richardson-Merrell was fined a total of $80,000. This is equivalent to a $40 levy on an individual earning $18,000 a year—obviously not much of a punishment. The company paid out substantially more, however, to the thousands of people who were injured by MER/29. Estimated at between $45 and $55 million ($15 million was covered by insurance), the damages amounted to approximately one year's pre-tax earnings for Richardson-Merrell during the period the drug was marketed.

The main reason the company paid as much as it did was that many of the lawyers with clients injured by MER/29 banded together in an unprecedented cooperative association known as the MER/29 Group. They were thus able to pool their efforts and resources to make their confrontation with Richardson-Merrell somewhat more even. The success of the MER/29 Group was made possible in large measure by the efforts of an energetic and idealistic young lawyer by the name of Paul D. Rheingold.

Paul Rheingold graduated in 1958 from the Harvard Law

* Mrs. Mary Rydgren commenting on why she and the other members of the jury in *Ostopowitz* v. *Richardson-Merrell* awarded $850,000 in punitive damages (plus $355,000 in compensatory damages) to a thirty-four-year-old woman who developed cataracts from MER/29 (reported in an article by Morton Mintz in the *Washington Post*, December 12, 1966).

151

School, where one of his classmates had been Ralph Nader. Although they did not know each other at the time ("Practically no one in the school knew him then," Rheingold recalled, "because he kept to himself") they would later become close friends. Rheingold handled Nader's famous invasion of privacy suit against General Motors, which the auto giant finally settled for $425,000.

Rheingold sees many parallels between the MER/29 litigation and Nader's action against General Motors. He told me that just as he could not imagine how culpable Merrell actually was until after the grand jury returned its indictment, he "had no idea of the depth of the GM's conduct" until after the investigator which the company had hired to snoop into Nader's affairs decided to cooperate. For example, when Senator Abraham Ribicoff's subcommittee which was investigating the whole affair asked General Motors why the company had placed Nader under surveillance, the company replied that they were merely concerned over Nader's allegations that the Corvair was unsafe but had meant to do him no harm. In fact, Rheingold told me, General Motors had instructed its investigator to find something in Nader's background, specifically something anti-Semitic, so they could blackmail him and cause his estrangement from Senator Ribicoff, who is Jewish. Rheingold confessed he "could never understand" why the subcommittee did not crack down on GM for what seemed like an obvious fraud on the Senate but then added sadly, "You know General Motors . . . there is politics involved and normal pressure."

Rheingold's successful tilt with General Motors was far in the future when in the early 1960's, as the twenty-nine-year-old assistant editor in chief of the *Journal* of the National Association of Claimants' Counsel of America (now known more simply if less accurately as the American Trial Lawyers), he began to receive inquiries from attorneys whose clients had been injured by MER/29. Rheingold was in charge of NACCA's product liability exchange—a service designed to put lawyers with similar cases against manufacturers in contact with one another—and he recalled that the questions came in even before the drug was removed from the market. Eventually MER/29 was withdrawn, and the initial trickle of inquiries turned into an avalanche. Early in 1963 a few of the attorneys realized that a lawsuit against Richardson-Merrell would be too complex and expensive to be successfully handled on an individual basis. They therefore suggested that those lawyers with MER/29 cases meet and determine whether it would be possible for them to share their knowledge and perhaps even their investigation costs. Rheingold agreed and, using his NACCA list, invited every lawyer who he knew had an MER/29 case to attend a meeting in Chicago on April 17, 1963. Surprisingly, Rheingold later reflected, "a great majority of them came."

The meeting was held at the Sherman House and was presided over by Lou Ashe, the partner of the flamboyant California trial attorney Melvin Belli. Rheingold and thirty-three lawyers with MER/29 cases sat around a huge table and revealed their mutual ignorance. The detailed grand jury indictment would not be returned for another nine months, and so while everyone knew, or thought they knew, that MER/29 had injured their clients (one of the lawyers present had himself developed cataracts as a result of taking the drug), no one knew even a hundredth of the true story. Many of the lawyers brought copies of the documents which they or Richardson-Merrell had filed in their cases, and much of the time was spent in trying to develop suitable legal theories with which to attack the pharmaceutical giant. The discussion had a futile ring to it, however, for legal theories could be worked out only if they had a clear understanding of the facts, and as of yet they did not. They were like desperately groping blind men attempting to make order of the jumble of rumors and suppositions.

The attorneys' ignorance as to the true nature of Merrell's liability (if any) for MER/29 was not unusual. The law recognizes that aggrieved litigants will often have only the vaguest idea of just *how* they were damaged by another's actions. Conversely, one accused of causing the injuries may similarly be ignorant of facts which might reveal a total lack of fault. The law therefore allows both sides to engage in what is called "discovery" proceedings. Simply stated, once a lawsuit is started, but before the case is actually tried before a judge and jury, each party is allowed to take the testimony of witnesses to the dispute, as well as of each other. The testimony is taken at semiformal proceedings called "depositions," often held in the offices of the attorney for one of the sides. The only people present are the lawyers, the person being "deposed," and a stenographer, who will later prepare a verbatim transcript.

In addition to the deposition, each party is given access to any relevant documents which may be in the possession of the other side. With respect to MER/29, the lawyers knew that if they each engaged in discovery on their own there would be much costly duplication of effort. Accordingly, everyone at the meeting generally agreed that they would explore the possibility of doing it together. Dues of $100 were levied, and the MER/29 Group was officially born. Of the thirty-three lawyers present at the meeting, thirty-one joined. Ultimately there were 288 members, many of whom had more than one client (three firms had over twenty clients, one had over a hundred). One of the members was deputized to approach Richardson-Merrell's lawyers and seek their cooperation in the Group's proposed unified discovery program. Paul Rheingold, who at one point was patronizingly referred to by Ashe as "our young friend," was elected "trustee" and was given responsibility for the Group's monies and for keeping the membership informed of developments. He was to be paid the modest rate of $10 an hour.

After a series of negotiations, and after they dismissed their first set of lawyers, Richardson-Merrell, who were anxious to avoid the expense and disruption of having their employees constantly giving testimony or preparing documents for each of the individual plaintiffs, agreed to cooperate with the MER/29 Group's plan for joint discovery. The accord was reached in a deserted Manhattan on Monday, November 25, 1963, the day President Kennedy was buried. Under the terms of the agreement, the Group would take the necessary depositions and transcripts would be made available to each member for use in his individual case. Richardson-Merrell agreed to give the Group access to all 107,000 documents relating to MER/29 which it had surrendered to the grand jury (the indictment had not yet been issued). The Group was to make copies of any document deemed to be relevant and supply them to its members. In short, the Group was to be an information gathering and dispensing unit for its members, relieving Richardson-Merrell of the obligation of complying with numerous "discovery" requests. The arrangement proved so convenient for Richardson-Merrell that when attorneys who were not members of the MER/29 Group sought to depose its employees or requested certain documents, they were urged by the company to join.

Although Rheingold would later modestly admit that in the beginning he was "just a bookkeeper," he assumed the major role in making the MER/29 Group work. He spent two summers wading through the relevant sections of the 107,000 documents (he said that he only was able to look at approximately 50,000) and collated the important ones into various packages together with complete instructions as to how they could be effectively used at a trial. Although the Group had hired an attorney to take the various depositions (at $35 an hour), Rheingold, by virtue of his greater knowledge of the complexities of the MER/29 story, did most of the deposition work too (at the bargain $10 an hour—this was raised to $20 effective January 1, 1965).

All told, the MER/29 Group and Richardson-Merrell jointly participated in twelve depositions. Those deposed included Frank N. Getman, Merrell's president during the period MER/29 was developed and marketed but by then a vice-president of Richardson-Merrell; Philip Ritter, the Merrell vice-president in charge of promotion; Dr. Harold Peck, the Merck scientist who discovered that MER/29 was causing cataracts in dogs and rats; Beulah Jordan; J. Knox Smith, who as the acting head of Merrell's toxicology-pathology laboratory was King's predecessor; the FDA medical officer Dr. John O. Nestor; Dr. Van Maanen; Bruce Umberger, a technician in the toxicology-pathology laboratory; and Dr. William Hollander, one of the MER/29 clinical investigators. Strangely, neither side chose to take the deposition of MER/29's central figure: William M. King.

Surprisingly, not every lawyer with an MER/29 case joined the MER/29 Group, and even more surprisingly, not every member of the Group participated in the joint discovery program. Some were reluctant to spend the additional money, others were reluctant to agree to let Richardson-Merrell have complete access to their clients' medical histories, which was a prerequisite to participation. Still others were evidently afraid that they would lose control over their cases or that their prestige would suffer. These fears were unfounded.

For approximately one thousand dollars Group members participating in the joint discovery program received their cases on a silver platter. They received a copy of the six-volume New Drug Application, the relevant documents laboriously culled from Merrell's files together with a "key" as to how they could best be utilized, and the various depositions with their important sections highlighted and analyzed. Additionally, they received a constant stream of suggestions. A compilation of this material—all of it prepared by Rheingold—could accurately be entitled "How to Try an MER/29 Case in Several Easy Steps." Rheingold also conducted a series of "MER/29 schools"—seminars for those lawyers without the time or the inclination to burrow through the many thousands of pages of testimony and important documents unassisted—

and added some of the Group's members at the trials of their cases.

All in all, Group members not only had the distinction of joining in an unprecedented and successful legal experiment but also did better in their trials and in settling their cases than did non-members. Of the eleven cases tried to a conclusion, four resulted in verdicts for Richardson-Merrell. Only one of these losses was sustained by a Group member. Of the seven plaintiff victories, six were by Group members, and the jury verdicts in these six averaged over $360,000.* The one non-Group member's victory was for $20,000.

The initial victory by an MER/29 Group member was in Allen Toole's case. Richardson-Merrell, hoping to avoid big verdicts against it, was cleverly settling what it considered to be dangerous cases before they could be tried. For example, the lawsuit on behalf of the six-year-old boy who developed cataracts while undergoing MER/29 therapy at the Mayo Clinic was settled for $80,000 quite early. Richardson-Merrell similarly tried to settle Toole's case and offered $50,000. Toole's lawyer, John Herron, did not consider this satisfactory compensation to the young father of two, and the case went to trial. On April 27, 1965, a San Francisco jury awarded Toole a total of $675,000, of which $500,000 was designed to punish Richardson-Merrell.

Rheingold explained the Toole verdict in the Group newsletter by noting that Herron had tried "a simply superb case" by generating "anger against the defendants because of their callous and indifferent attitude toward the ultimate consumers of the drug." The $675,000 was the largest verdict ever awarded in San Francisco, and Rheingold confidently reported that similar good results could be achieved by other members of the Group. The trial judge left the $175,000 compensatory damage award intact, but he cut the punitive damage award in half. The total award of $425,000 was upheld

---

* $1,200,000; $675,000; $150,000; $117,000; $45,000; and $20,000.

on appeal, the court affirming that the jury had sufficient evidence to conclude that Merrell had "acted recklessly and in wanton disregard of possible harm to others in marketing, promoting, selling and maintaining MER/29 on the market in view of its knowledge of the toxic effect of the drug."

The *Toole* verdict was evidently a big shock to Richardson-Merrell, for the June 1965 issue of the Group newsletter reports that the company's initial reaction was to "cut off all" settlement negotiations and to "withdraw all pending offers" in some cities. As the shock wore off, and apparently after a high-level reappraisal of the situation, settlement negotiations were resumed. The company became very generous in some of its offers.

Then it was the MER/29 Group's turn to be shocked. On July 30, 1965, a Group member who had prepared his case very well and had confidently rejected a settlement offer of $60,000 lost the verdict. Commenting on this case later, Rheingold would recall that he was "really astounded."

Group members had now won one and lost one, and both sides settled with an earnestness which reflected the uncertainty felt by each. By September 1965 Richardson-Merrell claimed to have settled some 650 MER/29 cases. The December 1965 issue of the Group newsletter reported on settlements ranging from a high of $125,000 for a thirty-one-year-old man with cataracts to a low of $2,000 given to a person described only as "an old woman."

The next case to be tried was *Roginsky* v. *Richardson-Merrell*. Roginsky, who was sixty-six at the time of the trial, had taken MER/29 beginning in February 1961. In addition to the loss of some hair, which later partly grew back, he developed a dry, scaly skin condition in the summer of 1961. Although he stopped taking the drug in the following January, the skin condition did not clear until some three years later. In the fall of 1963 it was discovered that he had partial cataracts, which did not appreciably interfere with his vision.

Richardson-Merrell steadfastly refused to agree that Roginsky's ailments were caused by their drug. They pointed out that in contrast to the "classic" MER/29 case, Roginsky's skin condition did not clear a few months after the drug was discontinued and that his cataracts did not develop beyond the incipient stage. They argued that the partial cataracts were most likely the natural result of old age and not caused by MER/29, and accordingly refused to make any settlement offer.

On March 8, 1966, after a five-week trial during which Richardson-Merrell was represented by former federal judge and former United States Deputy Attorney General Lawrence E. Walsh, the jury awarded Roginsky a total of $117,000, $100,000 of which was designed to punish the company. In the March 15 issue of the Group newsletter Rheingold jubilantly reported that the case, which was tried by William F. X. Geoghan, Jr., a partner in the firm where Rheingold then worked, demonstrated that "the evidence of wrongdoing is so overwhelming" that juries can be expected to award "fair punitive damages in any type of case." Richardson-Merrell was naturally less pleased, and they filed an immediate appeal.

A month later Richardson-Merrell lost another one, this time in the federal court in Seattle, Washington. The plaintiff's injuries were of the "classic" MER/29 variety, and his lawyer had started the trial immediately after attending one of Rheingold's "MER/29 schools." The jury awarded his client $150,000 (all of it was termed compensatory because punitive damages are not allowed in Washington). Before the trial the company had wanted to settle the case for $50,000. In return for not having Richardson-Merrell appeal, the case was finally settled for $125,000.

The real blockbuster insofar as Richardson-Merrell was concerned was the *Ostopowitz* case, tried in Westchester County, New York, at the end of 1966. The plaintiff was a young woman who had been taking MER/29 experimentally, not to lower cholesterol but in an attempt to alleviate a serious hormonal imbalance known as Cushing's disease. She suffered the classic MER/29 injuries, including cataracts, and although the company attempted to argue that this was preferable to Cushing's disease, the jury awarded Mrs. Ostopowitz $1.2 million; $850,000 was designated as punitive damages.

The case was tried for Mrs. Ostopowitz by Geoghan (who also tried *Roginsky*) assisted by Rheingold, whose knowledge of the intricacies of the MER/29 story was so great that at one point the trial judge referred to him as the "court of last resort." Richardson-Merrell was represented by a local Westchester lawyer, reputedly a friend of the company's general counsel. In contrast to Geoghan's effective courtroom tactics and former judge Walsh's valiant efforts in *Roginsky*, Richardson-Merrell's case was badly tried. A juror, interviewed after the verdict was announced, commented how he and the other jurors waited "for the defense to come out" with some answer to the plaintiff's case, but that "it never came."

Although the case was a fiasco insofar as Richardson-Merrell was concerned, it did have some amusing incidents. One of the witnesses called for the defense was the inventor of the chemical which was destined to become MER/29, Frank Palopoli. Richardson-Merrell's attorney asked Palopoli to describe how he had formulated the drug, and the young chemist proudly went off into a wildly complicated story. He had just about reached the high point of his explanation ("We could buy at the time from chemical supply houses parabromomolcolulene [*sic*] and butylethene [*sic*] and these were reacted together to form the demetholated complex in which litheme bromide is split off of this compound and becomes part of this system here. It is called—") when the judge interrupted: "I am going to interject. Do you think, Mr. Dempsey, that the jury can possibly understand this?"

At another time, James Dempsey, evidently sensing the jury's anger against Richardson-Merrell, commented that the trial was "not a lynching" and that he hoped the jury agreed with him "that there is a place in our society for pharmaceutical companies." As if to emphasize their value, he then noted that because of our new modern drugs "nobody dies of pneumonia any more," evidently not knowing that close to 60,000 Americans died from that disease in 1965 and that almost 6,000 would die from it somewhere in the United States during the course of the trial.

As we have seen, one of Richardson-Merrell's excuses for not disclosing the results of certain of their experiments was that they believed they were permitted to exercise "scientific judgment" as to what was relevant and what was not. In order to make this excuse "live" for the jury, the company's lawyer related a little story about the artist Rockwell Kent:

> I was thinking about an incident that Rockwell Kent told about his youth up there in Maine. He said that they had to do some dynamiting on the farm where he was raised, so they brought the dynamite man around to the farm and he found, unfortunately, he couldn't do the dynamiting because the dynamite was frozen. So he said, "We all sat around the kitchen and he put the sticks of dynamite in the kitchen stove to thaw out. None of us were worried. None of us were disturbed or upset about it at all. When the time came, after he smoked a pipe or so, he reached into the stove, took the sticks of dynamite out, took care of the task at hand. We had confidence," he said, "that he knew what he was doing, and if he would take the dynamite out then he should take it out." That I think is a homey way of expressing what is scientific judgment. It is a question of confidence in the man that you have who reads the test, or performs the test.

The analogy between marketing MER/29 on the basis of Merrell's "scientific judgment" that the drug was safe and sitting in the kitchen with sticks of dynamite "thawing out" in the stove must have made a heady impression on the jury.

Perhaps the most startling incident during the *Ostopowitz* trial occurred when one of the lawyers for Richardson-Merrell took a capsule of MER/29, opened it up, and pointing to the white powder, said something about how harmless it was. He then tried to hand it to the jury's foreman. Rheingold says he can still recall "the revulsion on the person's face . . . he just refused to take it."

Although the *Ostopowitz* jury gave the plaintiffs over a million dollars, the trial judge reduced the punitive damages portion of the verdict from $850,000 to $100,000. Richardson-Merrell contended that the revised total of $455,000 was still excessive and appealed. The case was then settled for $235,000, and they withdrew their appeal.

One case which was not settled on appeal was *Roginsky*, and on April 4, 1967, the United States Court of Appeals in New York by a 2 to 1 decision held that punitive damages should not have been permitted. Accordingly, they limited Roginsky's recovery to the $17,000 in compensatory damages which the jury had awarded. In a decision written by Henry J. Friendly, the court, while ostensibly ruling that there was insufficient evidence of fraud to submit the punitive damages question to the jury,° made it clear that it did not generally approve of allowing punitive damages awards against corporations. The court noted that a multiplicity of such awards, possible where hundreds or thousands of people have been injured by a widely sold product, could very well destroy the company. Judge Friendly termed the punitive damages concept under such circumstances economic "overkill" and contended that it was not necessary to deter wrongful conduct. "Criminal penalties and heavy compensatory damages," he wrote, would be enough. Punitive damages could, the judge gloomily predicted, "end the business life of a concern that has wrought much good in the past and might otherwise have continued to do so in the future, with many innocent stock-

---

° We have already seen how the California appellate court in affirming an award of substantial punitive damages in *Toole* noted that "from all of the evidence the jury could find that [Richardson-Merrell] acted recklessly and in wanton disregard of possible harm to others in marketing, promoting, selling and maintaining MER/29 on the market in view of its knowledge of the toxic effect of the drug."

holders suffering extinction of their investments for a single management sin."

Since, if the evidence warrants them, punitive damages *are* allowed in New York, the court could not rest after expressing its personal distaste for the concept. Judge Friendly therefore, in a lengthy section of his opinion, tried to demonstrate that contrary to the decision of various other courts and juries throughout the country, Merrell's conduct was not deserving of economic punishment.

His summary of the evidence was clearly designed to prove his point. For example, instead of evaluating the evidence in a light most favorable to Roginsky, as the court admittedly was obligated to do when considering whether the punitive damages question should have been submitted to the jury, the court seemingly gave Richardson-Merrell the benefit of every doubt. Thus it accepted Richardson-Merrell's excuse for not reporting the cataracts observed in dogs 69 and 71 in February 1960. Judge Friendly wrote that "the whole study was worthless since the dogs were contaminated by distemper and viral hepatitis," apparently ignoring a November 3, 1959, memorandum from Fritz Holthaus, an assistant in King's laboratory, which noted that the distemper outbreak required that the 40 mg. dog study be redone "using 5 conditioned male beagles." Dogs 69 and 71 were part of that group, and Merrell's February 1960 submissions to the FDA reporting on this experiment noted that they had been immunized against both distemper and viral hepatitis.

Similarly, while the court conceded that Dr. McMaster was negligent in not quickly running down Dr. Corday's February 1961 report that MER/29 had given one of his patients cataracts, it contended that "McMaster's sloth would not support a finding of recklessness" because Merrell did not have "reason to be seriously apprehensive" that MER/29 was capable of causing human cataracts. Yet, as we have seen, Merrell's management in January 1961 was not only aware of the cataracts reported by Merck, but the company's vice-president and chief scientist, Dr. Werner, on February 15, 1961, asked the company librarian to research "the incidence of cataract in normal adults."

What Roginsky's petition for a rehearing, following the court's initial adverse decision, termed the "most indefensible" of all the court's findings, however, was Judge Friendly's view of why the drug was ultimately removed from the market: "Taking the evidence in the sense most favorable to [Roginsky], the utmost shown is that the raid [by Dr. Nestor and his FDA colleagues on April 9 and 10, 1962] may have accelerated the decision by a few days; there is nothing to warrant an inference that but for this [Merrell] would have continued marketing the drug in the face of increasing evidence of its cataractogenic qualities."

The petition for rehearing characterized Judge Friendly's assertion that the evidence was being considered "in the sense most favorable" to Roginsky as "laughable," and reminded the court of Getman's April 9 memorandum, dictated while the FDA inspection was in progress, in which he suggested that "a top level review of our proper approach to the continued marketing of MER/29" take place on "Thursday, April 26." The court was unmoved. In an unsigned supplemental opinion, it declared with the infallibility of one having the last word that it "fail[ed] to see" how the import of the memorandum was "inconsistent" with the company's version of the events leading up to the drug's withdrawal.

Despite the court's apparent sympathy for Richardson-Merrell's position, it too was evidently overwhelmed by the sheer volume of incriminating evidence, and Judge Friendly avowed that while "few human endeavors would escape without blemish from such searching scrutiny, the picture is not a pretty one." Yet the court excused Merrell's conduct as something to be expected in the business world, and therefore, presumably, to be tolerated. Judge Friendly wrote that "some weight must be given to the human tendency to follow a course of conduct once decided upon even when considerations have appeared that would have led to a different decision at the outset, a tendency particularly strong when large investments of both effort and money have been made . . . [citing as support for this proposition a paperback abridgement of William James's treatise, *Principles of Psychology*]."

Noting that while this "human tendency" would not insulate against punitive damages awards based on conduct "pushed to the point of recklessness," Judge Friendly warned that courts "should be careful not to set the scale too low when a discovery of social utility is under review." In other words, since a new drug is potentially more beneficial than, let us say, a new style of shoes, pharmaceutical companies are to be permitted greater latitude than are bootmakers even though the consequences of their profit-driven indifference may be far more serious. A poorly styled shoe may look ugly and it may hurt when it is worn, but it can be discarded with the mere loss of the purchase price. An inadequately tested drug, on the other hand, can kill.

If *Ostopowitz* was a shock to Richardson-Merrell and the result of the *Roginsky* appeal was a disappointment to the MER/29 Group, the *Space* trial in Binghamton, New York, was a disaster from both points of view. Former judge Walsh was back in the picture for Richardson-Merrell, and Geoghan again tried the case for the plaintiff. For every incriminating document which Geoghan read to the jury, Walsh would read ten innocuous ones. Walsh's plan was to demonstrate that while a certain memorandum or advertisement might appear damaging when singled out and highlighted for the jury, it would fade into its proper perspective when viewed in context. Therefore hundreds of tangentially relevant documents were laboriously read to the jury in the course of the trial, which lasted three months. At the end the jury awarded Space $20,000—which approximately equaled his attorneys' costs in trying the case. Richardson-Merrell's costs were many times greater.

While *Space* was being tried, juries awarded $45,000 in a

case which Rheingold personally tried in Nevada, and $20,000 in one tried by a non-Group member. These were the last cases to reach court. Both sides recognized that it was in their mutual self-interest to settle. The plaintiffs were wary of going through long, expensive trials without the certainty of receiving a large award, and Richardson-Merrell were reluctant to continue their runs through the gauntlet of expensive trials with their inherent risk of an *Ostopowitz*-type verdict. Also, they wanted to avoid the attendant bad publicity, and thus willingly settled cases for much more money than they had offered in the beginning. According to Rheingold, cases for which they would have offered no more than $25,000 in settlement at the outset, they were readily paying over $100,000 to dispose of at the end.

Over a thousand cases were ultimately settled for substantial sums, and as we have seen, Richardson-Merrell's total payout (including that covered by insurance) has been estimated at between $45 and $55 million. The MER/29 Group collected some $77,000 from its members in dues and copying charges for documents and depositions. The value received by the members was many times that. Richardson-Merrell obviously paid more in settlement to those lawyers who knew their cases and were prepared to go to trial. Those lawyers who declined to invest several hundred dollars in order to learn more about their cases by and large were forced to settle for a fraction of what they could have received.

By late 1966 the MER/29 Group had essentially fulfilled its major investigatory function and, although Rheingold continued to provide assistance and documents to members, it slowly faded away. In one of the last newsletters, Rheingold humorously noted that inasmuch as the MER/29 Group always seeemd to hold ad hoc meetings in conjunction with conventions of the American Trial Lawyers, he hoped that if the ATL ever held a convention in Aswan, Egypt, the MER/29 Group would be able to get reservations "at the 'New Cataract Hotel' which was recently opened there."

8

MER/32—Thalidomide

"The United States this time escaped by the skin of its teeth, so to speak." *

The year 1962 was a bad time for the Wm. S. Merrell Company. In April it withdrew MER/29; in March it recalled its brand of thalidomide (initially known as MER/32 but later given the trade name Kevadon) from the Canadian market and from over a thousand physicians in this country who had been given the drug in connection with various clinical investigation programs. Just a year earlier, Richardson-Merrell's annual report had touted MER/29 and Kevadon as two of Merrell's brightest new products.

Thalidomide was synthesized in 1953 by Chemie Grünenthal, a West German pharmaceutical company. Four years later when it was released for general nonprescription sale, it quickly became that country's most popular sleeping pill. It induced a deep, natural-like slumber and, in contrast to the barbiturate-based sleeping preparations, an overdose was not fatal. The drug was not only sold in the form of sleeping pills but was also concocted into a variety of medicinal compounds. It was added to aspirin and cough syrups, it was formulated into a liquid for children, and it was even recommended to alleviate morning sickness in pregnant women. This latter use was tragically ironic; thalidomide would be revealed as one of the most virulently teratogenic (monster-causing)

* Senator Hubert H. Humphrey after hearing how the FDA's Dr. Francis O. Kelsey managed to keep thalidomide off the U.S. market.

167

drugs which had ever been made available for public consumption. If taken early in pregnancy, thalidomide prevented the fetus from properly developing and the child would be born, along with other malformations, with pitiful seal-like flippers in place of arms and legs. In the September 1, 1962, issue of *Saturady Review*, John Lear, the magazine's science editor, described some of the deformed babies as being "mere cocoons of flesh," referring the reader to a gruesome photograph at the head of the article.

Thalidomide's ability to deform the unborn was not recognized until late in 1961. Prior to that time the drug was thought to be faultless, and Chemie Grünenthal licensed its production and sale in several foreign countries. In January 1959 Merrell obtained a license for the United States and Canada. Its New Drug Application for Kevadon was filed in September 1960. A month later the company, hopeful that the drug would be quickly approved, embarked on an ambitious pre-marketing promotional campaign in the guise of a clinical investigation program.

Just as military hospitals had been asked to do experimental work with MER/29, not for "honest clinical work" (as a Merrell vice-president explained to president Getman) but as "pre-marketing softening prior to the introduction of the product," and just as Merrell's salesmen were told to use the "MER/29 clinical trials to push 'wait and see' G.P.s" and get them to prescribe the drug for their patients, Merrell also utilized clinical investigations to promote its brand of thalidomide.

On October 25, 1960, forty-four members of Merrell's sales force gathered for a special two-day conference, during which the Kevadon Hospital Clinical Program was explained. The purpose of the plan was to introduce Kevadon to those of the nation's "most influential physicians" who were likely to prescribe the drug once it was put on the market. The salesmen were to persuade their "prime targets" ("the chiefs and senior members of the departments of medicine, surgery, anesthesiology, and obstetrics-gynecology") to test Kevadon on their hospitalized patients. To make the program more attractive to these busy M.D.s, the physicians were to be reassured that they could enlist in the program, and receive free supplies of the still experimental drug, without the necessity of submitting the results of their "investigations" if they did not want to take the time.

"Bear in mind," the salesmen were told, "that these are not *basic* clinical research studies. We have firmly established the safety, dosage and usefulness of Kevadon by both foreign and U.S. laboratory and clinical studies. This program is designed to gain widespread *confirmation* of its usefulness in a variety of hospitalized patients. If your work yields case reports, personal communications or published work, all well and good. But the main purpose is to establish local studies whose results will be spread among hospital staff members." The salesmen were thus warned not to "get involved by selling a basic clinical research program instead of Kevadon." If a physician was hesitant, they were told to "appeal to the doctor's ego—we think he is important enough to be selected as one of the first to use Kevadon in that section of the country."

On November 17, less than one month after the program was started, Merrell's goal was reached and the salesmen were directed via a special delivery letter to "cease fire—you made it." They were also told how to deal with the physician who wanted additional free supplies of the drug. "We do not want to continue these studies after the doctor has already convinced himself of Kevadon's advantages, but we are willing to send him a small additional supply to keep Kevadon in front of him until it becomes commercially available." No wonder Senator Humphrey was moved to condemn the Kevadon Hospital Clinical Program as "marketing," and "not clinical investigation."

By November 29, a little over two months after the New Drug Application was filed, Merrell's special Kevadon sales force established studies involving some 29,000 patients.

Although they were told that Kevadon's safety had already been established, at least one physician had some reservations. On December 5, 1960, Dr. Thomas Jones, who as the associate director of medical research in charge of Kevadon was Dr. McMaster's equivalent in Merrell's hierarchy, wrote the following reassuring letter:

> Dear Dr. Linton
>
> I have heard from our representative in your area, Mr. J. Walker, with regard to your question on the possible effect of Kevadon on the fetus. Unfortunately, I am unable to answer this question since it has not been established whether or not there is any transfer of Kevadon across the placental barrier. However, we feel that, even if transfer does occur, it would be completely safe . . .

This reassuring letter was written one year before Merrell would learn of thalidomide's terrible ability to deform the human embryo.

Merrell informed its special Kevadon sales force that it expected the drug to be marketed in the United States early in 1961. The Canadian Food and Drug Directorate approved Kevadon's application shortly after it was filed, allowing the drug to be marketed there in April 1961, but the United States Food and Drug Administration would prove to be more cautious.

Kevadon's New Drug Application was assigned to a recently arrived physician in the FDA's New Drug Branch by the name of Francis Kelsey. As fate would have it, she shared an office with Dr. John Nestor at the time he was involved with MER/29, and both of them came to know Merrell's liaison man, Dr. F. Joseph Murray, very well. When it was apparent that Dr. Kelsey was not going to approve Kevadon's NDA as rapidly as Merrell would have liked, Dr. Murray, in between trying to forestall adverse action by the FDA in connection with MER/29, kept the pressure on. He, at times together with other representatives of Merrell, was in constant contact with Dr. Kelsey in an attempt to get her favorable decision.

As Dr. Kelsey later remembered, they "came to Washington, it seemed, in droves. They wrote letters and telephoned —as often as three times a week. They telephoned my superiors and they came to see them too." A superior would later recall that when "they got too thick around Dr. Kelsey, I would just come in with my little hatchet and clear them out." Despite the pressure ("most of the things they called me you just couldn't print," she told an interviewer, she remained firm to her conviction. She would not be rushed.

A month after Kevadon's New Drug Application had been filed, Dr. Kelsey wrote a long and detailed letter to Merrell which in substance declared that the application was incomplete and inadequately demonstrated safety. She later recounted that her major concern at that point was that while Kevadon induced sleep in humans, it did not seem to have this effect in the test animals. Thus, she reasoned, the fact that the drug was safe in animals did not necessarily mean it was safe in humans. Dr. Kelsey therefore asked Merrell to submit additional information on the pharmacological properties of the drug together with more detailed reports of human case histories. When this information was submitted, Dr. Kelsey asked her husband, a physician/pharmacologist who was a special assistant to the Surgeon General, to analyze some of the more technical data. He did, and his memorandum dated December 30, 1960, blasted Merrell for compiling "an interesting collection of meaningless pseudoscientific jargon apparently intended to impress chemically unsophisticated readers." At another point he noted that a comparison which the company had made violated "an elementary concept of pharmacology," and he could not "believe this to be honest incompetence."

On February 1, 1961, Dr. Murray informed Dr. Kelsey that Merrell wanted to release Kevadon on March 6 and would appreciate it if she could quickly approve the New Drug Application so they could proceed with printing the labels. Dr. Kelsey said that she would do her best. On February 15 Dr. Murray complained to one of Dr. Kelsey's superiors to say that he was being pressed by Merrell's management to get the NDA approved so the company would have time to brief their sales force. On the next day he again pressured Dr. Kelsey, and this is her memorandum recording the conversation: "Dr. Murray called. He said he had spoken to Dr. Smith yesterday. He wondered about Kevadon. I said I hoped to get to it next week. He said last time I spoke to him I said I would get to it next day. I assured him I had never been that optimistic. He agreed he had probably misunderstood me."

A week later, while looking through several issues of the *British Medical Journal* Dr. Kelsey came across two letters to the editor which caused her some concern. The first letter appeared in the December 31, 1960, issue and was entitled "Is Thalidomide to Blame?" In it a physician reported that four of his patients taking thalidomide had experienced abnormal numbing and tingling sensations in their hands and feet. The second letter, written by a representative of the company selling thalidomide in Great Britain, appeared in the January 14, 1961, issue and responded to the first. He admitted that his company was receiving similar reports from other physicians and explained that the symptoms described a potentially serious inflammation of the nerves in the hands and feet known as peripheral neuritis. As the company "felt satisfied" that thalidomide could be the cause, he wrote, they had included a warning to that effect in their literature since August 1960. Indeed, the company's advertisements warned that the drug should be immediately discontinued at the first appearance of the symptoms.

This correspondence connecting thalidomide with nerve damage alerted Dr. Kelsey to the possibility that the drug might not be as safe as everyone thought, and might cause other, as yet unknown, side effects. "Because of this peripheral neuritis, we were particularly concerned with the possible effects to the fetus, which might be exposed to the drug for a prolonged period of time," she later testified.

When Dr. Murray inquired on February 23, 1961, about her progress with the Kevadon application, Dr. Kelsey told him that she was concerned over thalidomide's possible association with peripheral neuritis. Dr. Murray replied that Merrell had seen the reports "and had written for further information." However, the British were "merely adding a warning" to their literature, he told her, and urged that the Food and Drug Administration permit Merrell to do the same. Dr. Kelsey refused, explaining that she was reluctant to release Merrell's thalidomide for sale until she knew more about the drug.

In early March Dr. Murray and Dr. Jones flew to Europe to study some of the nerve-damage reports. On their return they reassuringly explained to Dr. Kelsey that the problem was not very significant, since it affected only one half of one percent of the people who took the drug, and argued that this minor drawback was greatly outweighed by thalidomide's advantages over the barbiturate sedatives. They therefore urged her to approve Kevadon's New Drug Application without delay and thus permit Merrell to proceed with its marketing and promotion plans. In her written memorandum of this meeting Dr. Kelsey recorded: "I had the feeling throughout that they were at no time being wholly frank with me and that this attitude has obtained in all our conferences etc. regarding this drug," but admitted that she might be "partly prejudiced" because Merrell's advance publicity had featured work which "we indicated was inadequate" and by "their failure to notify us of the British reports of toxicity."

Five days later Dr. Murray wrote Dr. Kelsey again and argued that the application should be quickly approved because Merrell had already provided "adequate documentary proof" of its "relative safety." Murray reminded her that Merrell "originally submitted the new drug application approximately seven months ago" and that he was "hopeful" that she would review the material at an early date and advise him of her decision by telephone as soon as possible. At around the same time Dr. Kelsey received a letter from one of Merrell's Kevadon clinical investigators stating that he was "surprised to learn the other day from Dr. Tom Jones of the Wm. S. Merrell Co. that their application" to market the drug "had been delayed" and urging Dr. Kelsey to approve what he termed "an outstandingly safe medication." She replied that she was not yet satisfied that Kevadon "has been demonstrated to be safe."

On April 13 Dr. Murray complained to Dr. Smith about the delay in getting Kevadon released for sale. His superiors at Merrell, he said, were beginning to think that he was not applying enough pressure to get the application approved. The next day he called Dr. Smith again, asking if there were any new developments. When told that there were none, Dr. Murray related how Merrell's officers thought that the usual methods were not paying off and that they were considering approaching the FDA commissioner personally. Dr. Smith explained that things could not be hurried, prophetically noting that it "often happened that side effects of drugs were not reported until they had been on the market for some time."

On April 19 Dr. Murray tried yet another time. In a stern note to Dr. Kelsey he reiterated that the drug was safer than barbiturates and submitted documentation designed to show that not only was the incidence of the alleged thalidomide-caused peripheral neuritis "exceedingly small" but that the medical history of that particular disorder indicated that it was a side effect common to many drugs and that "it almost invariably" cleared up immediately upon discontinuance of therapy. "There is actually no proof thalidomide causes peripheral neuritis," but the evidence was merely "circumstantial in that patients with the condition improved upon removal of the drug," he stressed. "In order that we may intelligently proceed with our market plans, I should like to have you advise me of your final decision on this new drug application some time next week."

On May 5 Dr. Kelsey answered. Obviously peeved at the incessant pressure, she wrote that the New Drug Application was "entirely inadequate to establish the safety of Kevadon tablets."

> We have taken appropriate note of your contention that it has not been proved that Kevadon tablets actually cause peripheral neuritis, and the fact that the [proposed package insert] fails to make a frank disclosure that the drug has been found to cause peripheral neuritis. In consideration of an application for a new drug, the burden of proof that the drug causes side effects does not lie with this Administration. The burden of proof that the drug is safe, which must include adequate studies of all the manifestations of toxicity which medical or clinical experience suggest, lies with the applicant. In this connection, we are much concerned that apparently evidence with respect to the occurrence of peripheral neuritis in England was known to you but not forthrightly disclosed in the application.

When he received the letter, Dr. Murray complained to Dr. Smith that it was "somewhat libelous."

Meanwhile, Kevadon was being sold on a prescription basis in Canada and Merrell was advertising it as providing "safe, sound sleep." Unlike the British firm, it did not disclose in its advertisements that the drug was thought to cause peripheral neuritis.

Merrell kept the pressure on to get the drug approved in the United States. They were hoping to market Kevadon in the middle of November 1961. Toward that goal they arranged in September for members of their scientific staff, including Dr. Van Maanen, and several of the Kevadon clinical investigators to meet with Dr. Kelsey in an attempt to neutralize her doubts as to the drug's safety. They did not succeed. In her memorandum of the conference she recorded that one of the clinical investigators told of a patient who developed peripheral neuritis while on Kevadon and who was "still not completely cured over a year later." When she asked the assembled experts how Kevadon might affect the human embryo they said "they had no knowledge of what this drug might do to the fetus if used in pregnant women and admitted the cases so far were too few to be significant." One of the investigators "expressed some skepticism as to whether the drug really could live up to its initial reputation of non-toxicity" over the short term.

Several weeks after the conference Dr. Murray again asked Drs. Smith and Kelsey to quickly approve the NDA because Merrell still hoped to be able to market the drug by mid-November. They refused to be hurried, however, and Dr. Kelsey informed Murray that she now wanted the drug's brochure to carry a statement warning against its use by pregnant women. Her concern at this stage was still theoretical.

Dr. Kelsey's theoretically based fears were well founded. On November 29, 1961, two days before they would mail their MER/29 warning letter, Merrell received a cablegram from Chemie Grünenthal telling them that the West German company had removed thalidomide from the market because the drug was suspected of causing serious birth defects. On November 30 Dr. Murray informed Dr. Kelsey, commenting that he hoped the reported association would turn out to be merely coincidental. Several days later thalidomide's British manufacturer, concerned over the reports they were receiving, followed the lead of the German company and withdrew their brand of thalidomide from the market. Merrell was evidently not convinced that the situation was serious enough to warrant withdrawal. They did, however, send the following warning letter to every physician in Canada:

Dear Doctor:

We have received information from abroad on the occurrence of congenital malformations in the offspring of a few mothers who had taken thalidomide (marketed in Canada as Kevadon) early in their pregnancies. It is impossible at this time to determine whether, in fact, there is any causal relationship.

However, until definitive information is available to us, as a precaution we are adding the following contraindication to the use of Kevadon:

> Kevadon should not be administered to pre-menopausal women who may become pregnant.

We are actively following this matter and you will be advised when it is finally determined whether or not this precautionary step was necessary.

The letter was mailed on December 5. On December 4 a similar letter was sent to those clinical investigators in this country whom Merrell considered "active." Physicians who had received the drug but were not considered to be active investigators were apparently not contacted.

While Merrell was professing uncertainty as to thalidomide's role in the deformities, the hitherto rare and almost unknown seal-flipper malformation * was approaching pandemic proportions among the babies of those women who had taken the drug early in their pregnancy. As early as January 6, 1962, Dr. Widukind Lenz, a West German physician who was among the first to associate thalidomide with the malformations, estimated that between two and three thousand thalidomide-deformed babies had been born in his country since 1959. Yet on February 21, 1962, in a letter which Merrell's president, Frank N. Getman, would later characterize as "reemphasizing" the December 5 warning, the company informed Canadian physicians that there was "still no positive

---

* In her exhaustive article in the June 30, 1962, issue of the *Journal of the American Medical Association*, Dr. Helen Taussig, who toured West Germany studying the outbreak of deformities, reported that "Dr. Grüber of Gottingen, who is now 86 years old and has devoted his life to malformations in man and animals, told me he had seen as many individuals with two heads as he had with [the seal-flipper type of deformity]."

proof of a causal relationship between the use of thalidomide
during pregnancy and malformations in the newborn" and
that it was "encouraging to note that studies in pregnant rats
have not shown a single malformation in more than 1,100
offspring of thalidomide-treated animals." The company did
note, however, that because of the uncertainty the "contraindication stated in our December 5th letter is still necessary."
They did not withdraw the drug.

Dr. Kelsey's fear that because thalidomide did not put
the test animals to sleep, they might also not develop the
same side effects as humans was proven correct. Pregnant
rats given thalidomide did not give birth to malformed
young, but pregnant rabbits who were later given the drug
did. One of the tragedies of the thalidomide episode was that
the drug obviously had been tested in the wrong animals.

The February 23 issue of *Time* magazine headlined the
thalidomide story in the "Medicine" section ("Sleeping Pill
Nightmare") and revealed that the drug was still being sold
in Canada. Amid the resulting furor the chief of Canada's
Food and Drug Directorate replied that thalidomide did not
have to be withdrawn because Canada "has no cases yet" and
the drug's association with the deformities was "only statistical." An FDD spokesman told inquiring newsmen that pre-
cipitous action was not required ("You shouldn't jump off the
deep end," he was quoted as saying) and that Merrell's two
warning letters were "adequate." A week later they changed
their minds. On March 2 the Food and Drug Directorate asked
Merrell to recall the drug, and the company agreed. Unbe-
lievably, some pharmacists, estimated by *MacLean's* magazine at between 10 and 15 percent, refused to relinquish the
drug. One druggist, when asked by the magazine why he was
still selling thalidomide as late as April 10, replied "Why not?
It's safe for an adult male, isn't it?" When told that any drug
lying around the house might be taken unknowingly by a
pregnant woman, he replied, "That's not my problem. I'm not

sending back the rest of the supply until people stop asking for it."

On March 8, 1962, just over a month before it would re-call MER/29 from the market, Merrell told the FDA it was withdrawing its New Drug Application for Kevadon. In a lengthy letter dated August 10, 1962, directed to "All Physi-cians," Merrell president Getman explained why he believed the facts of the thalidomide story demonstrated that "Merrell has vigorously pursued a course that is in the best interest of the public welfare, both in terms of human safety and sci-entific and medical research." He summarized the "significant events in the thalidomide history" from Chemie Grünenthal's synthesis of the drug in 1953, through Merrell's receipt of the cablegram informing them of the drug's association with birth defects, their notification of the United States Food and Drug Administration and the Canadian Food and Drug Di-rectorate, and their sending of the various warning letters, to early in March when they withdrew the drug in Canada and stopped the clinical testing in the United States. "Thalido-mide had never been available in the United States except for clinical and animal investigation," Getman explained. It was not, however, due to their lack of trying.

On July 31 Senator Kefauver, one of the prime movers for the improvement of the Food and Drug laws, condemned the "zeal of the Wm. S. Merrell Co. to get thalidomide on the U.S. market, its non-cooperative attitude toward the FDA displayed throughout the file, and its continuous and high-handed pressures on the physician handling the application, Dr. Francis Kelsey." As with MER/29, the company was reluctant to see its investment of time and money in thalido-mide go to waste. Thus, even after Chemie Grünenthal and its British licensee, concerned over the association of thalido-mide with the increasing number of deformities, withdrew the drug in late November and early December 1961, Mer-rell was content to issue a warning letter. Furthermore, in a memorandum to the president of Richardson-Merrell, H. Robert Marschalk, dated December 12, 1961, Frank Getman foresaw the possibility of the company still being allowed to market the drug in the United States. He noted that while projected sales for Kevadon in Merrell's original budget for fiscal year 1961–62 "has been entirely eliminated," a new estimate could be made "if we are able to get an [effective] NDA in the spring."

Despite the fact that as late as February 21 Merrell was telling Canadian physicians that there was "still no positive proof" that thalidomide was causing the deformities and that it was "encouraging" that the offspring of pregnant rats given the drug were not deformed, Merrell's director of medical research, Carl A. Bunde, was able to write in the August 10, 1962, issue of *Life* magazine (in a statement headlined ". . . A U.S. Drug Firm's Shock") that "we have not minimized the possibility that thalidomide may be connected with congenital malformation in some way not now understood." In his letter of the same date to this nation's physicians Getman reiterated that "we have not at any time minimized the possible relationship between thalidomide and congenital malformations" and concluded: "We hope this series of events will lead to better scientific understanding of the development of the human embryo and to progress in preventing fetal abnormalities, whatever the cause. We plan to do everything in our power to help assure this outcome."

This latter statement is strangely reminiscent of a paragraph in Getman's April 17, 1962, letter announcing MER/29's withdrawal from the market: "As you probably know, Merrell has had and will continue to have an extensive research program in cardiovascular disease. MER/29 has been one important phase of this effort. The work on this compound by us and many others has made contributions to basic knowledge in this field." Just as this was small comfort to those with MER/29-induced cataracts, Getman's panegyric reference to thalidomide's role in the advancement of scientific knowledge must have been small comfort to those mothers and fathers of deformed infants.

That this country in large measure was spared the thalidomide tragedy was due to Dr. Kelsey. On August 7, 1962, President Kennedy awarded her the Distinguished Federal Civilian Service Award for "her high ability and steadfast confidence in her professional decision."

9

Aftermath

"Richardson-Merrell's Pres. H. Robert Marschalk
and Merrell Div.'s Pres. Frank N. Getman say the
reputations of both the division and the parent
company seem to have come through relatively
untarnished." *

From July 1960 to June 1961, the only complete fiscal year
MER/29 was marketed, Merrell sold approximately $9 million
worth of the drug. This was just under 6 percent of Richardson-Merrell's sales of $151.5 million, and almost a third of
Merrell's $28.3 million. On December 12, 1961, less than two
weeks after the issuance of the warning letter, Getman estimated in a memorandum to Marschalk that "the cutbacks of
MER/29 and Kevadon [will] immediately reduce our [Mer-
rell's] profit before taxes $3,125,000." Merrell's after-tax prof-
its attributable to MER/29 alone for fiscal year 1960–61 were
over $1 million. As far short as all this was from the com-
pany's ecstatically optimistic projection of sales in the hundreds of millions of dollars (or even billions, if they could
persuade everyone over thirty-five or forty to take the drug),
MER/29 was still a very important cog in Merrell's operations. Its recall, and thalidomide's, coupled with the adverse
publicity and uncertainty as to the ultimate disposition of the
backlogged damage claims (estimated at one point to ap-

---

* *Business Week*, September 15, 1962, p. 921, commenting on the impact
of MER/29 and Kevadon on Richardson-Merrell and the Wm. S. Merrell Co.
division.

proach $1 billion *), depressed the price of Richardson-Mer-
rell's stock for several years.

Merrell and its parent corporation also lost prestige in
the medical community. For a period of time at least, the
Food and Drug Administration operated under a policy of
not considering Merrell's submissions "reliable without thorough verification." The FDA's Dr. Kessenich also noted that
Merrell was but one of many Richardson-Merrell subsidiaries
and that since the FDA did not "know whether or not the unreliability of data submitted by the Wm. S. Merrell Co. is
characteristic of the operations of these related firms" it could
not "reasonably assume" that the information submitted by
them was reliable without "special handling."

Many physicians too must have been disturbed by the apparent unreliability of Merrell's pronouncements. Others were
undoubtedly angered by the high-pressure promotional tactics employed. An Iowa physician, in a letter of complaint
written to Merrell in August 1962, told how two of the company's salesmen attempted to persuade him to prescribe
MER/29 by being "quite insistent that 'any real good physician' would be using" the drug. "I can still recall," he wrote,
"the indignation which these two representatives showed"
when he told them that he was unimpressed. The physician
thought "it would be extremely wise for all of us concerned
to take perhaps a *little longer* look at some of the proposed
kinds and types of suggested treatments before 'diving' in
with all fours."

On April 23, 1962, one week after Getman announced
that MER/29 was being withdrawn, an Illinois physician
angrily wrote him the following:

> When this drug came out you were so anxious to get this
> latest boon to humanity into the hot, anxious hands of the
> physicians that you sent out your propaganda via Western
> Union. I remember it well because I made an extra trip to
> the telegraph office after a hard day's work to pick up this

* *Business Insurance*, September 23, 1968, p. 17.

bonanza, tricked into thinking that it was something important.

Fortunately, this incident poisoned my mind and I have not had the fortune to use a drug whose action is now found to be unnecessary and whose side effects are deleterious.

Government control is a nasty word to me and I am sure, to you. I wonder if my *research* would be *objective* if I had a million dollars riding on coming up with the "right" answer. Incidents like this seem to indicate the necessity for some sort of *objective research before new products are released.*

I hope you have better luck with future products. I know I will be circumspect in the use of anything bearing your brand name.

Others felt a more personal anger. There were those like Allen Toole who trustingly took MER/29 at the direction of their physicians only to discover that it robbed them of their sight. Paul Rheingold conservatively estimated that over 5,000 people were injured by the drug, but lamented that a relatively small percentage ever sought redress from Merrell. In an excellent article on the MER/29 litigation, written in 1968 and published in the *California Law Review,* he explained that many were not aware that the drug caused their injuries while others thought that it would somehow be improper to take Merrell to court. This latter group, Rheingold noted, included a judge, a congressman, an editor of a major newspaper, and a famous entertainer.

But there were those who were not reluctant to sue. The following letter, dated December 27, 1963, written to Senator Humphrey and published by his committee, is perhaps illustrative of their views:

Dear Senator:

Naturally, I listened and read with a great deal of interest the decision of the Federal grand jury pertaining to the suit against the William S. Merrell Company of Cincinnati, the manufacturers of the drug, MER/29.

I am one of the unfortunate and am positive it gave me two cataracts. I had one removed April 2, 1963, from my right eye, and a cataract was removed from the left eye on December 3, 1963. So, on Christmas Day, I am in a convalescing period as a result of the second operation . . .

I am suing the company and I intend to pursue this suit with all the vigor I have because destroying me of my sight has just put me out of business. In my type of livelihood, I must have my eyesight to see the type of [products] that I purchase. No payment financially would be enough to compensate me for the pain, suffering, and inconvenience that I have gone through and am still going through. So, please, Senator, keep pushing them with all the strength and guts you have. They deserve to be punished.

While the MER/29 mosaic is composed of many individual tragedies, the one which stands out in my mind concerns the case of a twenty-three-year-old medical student (whom I will call Peter) whose devotion to medical research prompted him to take large amounts of MER/29 experimentally. An important part of drug research entails assaying a compound's activity in a healthy human body, where its effect will not be masked by illness. Prisoners and other paid volunteers are most frequently used for this, but often the investigating physician will first test the drug on himself. Naturally, it is given to healthy humans only if prior experience, usually with animals, indicates that there will be little or no risk of serious complications.°

In early 1961 a highly respected physician and medical researcher (whom I will call Dr. A.) was investigating the effect of large doses of MER/29 on one of the more important bodily functions. He hoped the drug would prove beneficial in treating a family of serious disorders. Merrell approved of his work and supplied sufficient quantities of the drug for his study. For a period of time Dr. A. personally took four grams of MER/29 a day (sixteen times the normal daily dose of 250

° The use of an experimental drug of doubtful safety as a last-ditch attempt to save the life of one otherwise beyond hope is, of course, another matter. There the risk may be outweighed by the possible benefits. Thus, while an anti-cancer drug suspected of being able to kill 20 percent of the people to whom it is given will be a permissible therapeutic agent in terminal cases, it should not be tested on normal individuals.

milligrams). In the middle of February 1961 Peter, who was one of Dr. A.'s students at medical school and who was assisting him with the study, volunteered to take one gram of the drug every day. On April 12 this dose was increased to one and a half grams. Two weeks later Peter's hair had turned lighter in color and his skin seemed dryer than normal. On May 15 he reported that his eyes felt as if they were being irritated by some foreign object. Dr. A., now very concerned, immediately stopped giving Peter the drug and placed him under a treatment which he hoped would prevent further eye trouble. When he informed Merrell they reassured him that there was nothing to worry about.

By the middle of June, Peter developed a severe and painful irritation of the iris. Dr. A. again called Merrell. This time he was more agitated and demanded to know whether they had ever heard of anyone getting iritis from the drug. Merrell said no and told him not to get "hysterical." Dr. A. replied that if he sounded hysterical it was because he had given the drug to a perfectly normal person, which he would not have done had he suspected that there was the slightest possibility of serious side effects. Merrell attempted to reassure him, and on June 28, 1961, Dr. Bunde, director of medical research, wrote him the following letter:

[We have learned] that the many rumors and comments flying around frightened you and you had decided to discontinue your large-dose experiments temporarily.

I want to comment on this, and I hope you will accept this as an opinion based on having available many more data than any one or dozen investigators could have, and also, in part, from experience in tracking down some of these rumors . . . I also hope you can interpret this as being restrained to the extent of most of all wanting to protect our investigators from getting into any trouble, using MER/29 or any of our drugs experimentally. I find in most cases that I am more cautious than our investigators.

Up to the present, we have had no evidence which could reasonably associate MER/29 therapy with [liver] toxicity . . .

After MER/29 had been on the market for some six months or more, we began receiving reports of hair loss. These were isolated and mixed with reports of hair growth and color changes, so that it was difficult at first to decern [*sic*] a pattern or determine if the condition were truly drug-related. We immediately started a more intensive investigation of all complaints . . . and soon concluded that, at least in some of the cases, the hair loss was related to MER/29 therapy . . . We immediately changed our literature to include this under side effects.

Before the drug was put on the market, dryness, or scaliness, or a rash-like condition had been reported in a certain number of patients. This was listed under the term *dermatitis* as a side effect in the original literature. We have heard of a few cases since, most of them recently, where this dermatitis has been of a very severe nature . . . some of these were [found to be] not related to the drug. At any rate, we are recognizing that if mild cases of dermatitis can occur, an occasional rare case will be severe. The two most severe cases which we have tracked down are the least likely to be drug-related. One was the case reported by Corday and which he has been ballyhooing around the country as if it had been an epidemic. This patient was on at least three other drugs known to produce allergic [skin] reactions and had a previous history of [skin problems] . . .*

We had further reports that MER/29 affected coagulation time of blood [but these proved to be without substance] . . .

The only other complaint that we have received in more than six instances, which we use as our arbitrary number for being watchful, is the loss of libido . . .

The above is as accurate a summary and interpretation of our total experience with MER/29 toxicity as I can give you at this time. I will say that if you use the large doses you should exert extra precautions, especially in looking for the earliest manifestation of those effects that now appear to be drug-related. Most specifically these are: a type of dermatitis, loss of hair, and change in hair color.

Although purportedly disclosing Merrell's "total experience with MER/29 toxicity," Bunde did not mention the cataracts

---

* Merrell would later pay Dr. Corday's patient $50,000 for his injuries.

which Merck had seen in their animals, known to Merrell in January 1961, nor did he mention Dr. Corday's early February report that his patient had developed cataracts. Furthermore he did not disclose that Merrell had investigated the incidence of human cataract formation and was thus apparently concerned that this too might be an MER/29-related side effect.

By the middle of June, Peter's iritis had cleared and slit-lamp examinations failed to reveal changes in the lens. By February 1962 Dr. A. was breathing a little easier and hoped that the danger had passed. Then, in April, Peter complained of foggy vision. A slit-lamp examination on April 16, at about the time Merrell announced that it was withdrawing MER/29 from the market out of an "abundance of caution," showed up tiny opacities in the lens of each eye. The cataracts developed rapidly, and by the end of the school year Peter was almost totally blind. They were removed in two operations, the first during the early summer of 1962 and the second during Christmas vacation.

Dr. A. was grief-stricken. He related to me how he would never have given the drug had he known that there was a possibility of eye trouble. "I trusted them," he said, referring to Merrell. "If they had told me what they knew at the time, this would never have come about . . . I deeply resent them." Dr. A. tried to help Peter, for whom he now felt responsible, the best way he could. "I got him through his junior year of medical school. I bought these screen things, he could see well enough to see the screen, and I tutored him in my home." Dr. A. also bought other special equipment for Peter and arranged for his medical care.

Although Merrell was initially reluctant to accept financial responsibility for his injuries, they eventually did and today Peter is a practicing physician with the aid of man-made contact lenses to replace the lenses which MER/29 destroyed. He is able to see with about a 5 percent distortion of vision.

Like his former student, Dr. A. is still scarred by the incident, although his lesions are emotional rather than physical. "I very nearly quit research because of this," he related. Dr. A. admitted that although he blames Merrell for not being absolutely candid ("I don't know what they were thinking of, not telling me what was going on"), he cannot pretend that he is totally innocent. "Those were pretty heady times. We had made a kind of a breakthrough—we thought. One was willing at that time to do things perhaps he wouldn't have if he had this sobering experience somewhere along the line." And a sobering experience it was. Although Dr. A. defends the necessity for drug research in normal individuals, he cautions that the compounds should first be more thoroughly researched. He says he still keeps a picture of his former student on his desk "with his white hair . . . to remind me to be careful."

Almost immediately after Merrell announced that it was withdrawing MER/29 from the market, Dr. McMaster called several leading heart specialists and researchers to get their views. According to McMaster's memorandum of April 16, 1962, Dr. Irving S. Wright, who had been chairman of Merrell's 1959 Princeton Conference, "repeated his previous statement that he believes Merrell was a bit too hasty in getting MER/29 on the market in the first place." This was, of course, what the cautionary statements found in the evaluations of MER/29 by *The Medical Letter* and in the *Journal of the American Medical Association* were all about. It was what the famed heart specialist Dr. Paul Dudley White cautioned against when in February 1960 he wrote Merrell: "Certainly if MER/29 is safe and effective we ought to know about it and be using it, but I suppose we will need much more time to be absolutely sure." And it was what Dr. Robert W. Wilkins prophetically condemned when he stated at the Princeton Conference that drug companies were "reluctant to accept . . . that you cannot tell what a drug will do after four or five years of treatment without waiting four or five years."

There is more to the MER/29 story than the hasty marketing of an unproven drug; there are the documented instances of misrepresentations and half truths by which the company attained FDA approval for the drug and promoted its use to the medical profession. Indeed, at times the whole story seems unreal. Thus, when in the *Ostopowitz* trial a Merrell character witness, Dr. Jean K. Weston, director of the American Medical Association's drug division, was confronted with evidence of Merrell's laxity, he refused to believe it:

Q: Would you assume, just for this question, that the compounds are essentially the same, Merck's compound and MER/29, and would you assume, sir, that Merck's animals developed these cataracts, and would you assume, sir, that by this time Richardson-Merrell knew about the 25 out of their 36 rats developing what they called corneal opacities, that two dogs developed cataracts, which they did not report to the government, and one dog had this [eye] exudation; and assume further that reports had come in from the field from humans of tearing of the eyes, blurring of vision and so forth from humans?

Now sir, was it in accordance with proper standards and practices right at that point in January of 1961 when Merck told them what they did, not to report that to either the government, the medical profession or the clinical investigators?

[After procedural objections, the question was answered.]
A: That is a rather complex question for anyone to attempt to answer, because it involves so many aspects of the studies which were carried out on this particular agent.

I feel that to answer that question with a simple yes or no is—would be for me to assume that indeed all these hypotheses were actualities, and I cannot in my own experience now conceive of a situation which I personally have been in or which I know about in the industry where this has happened.

What Dr. Weston could not "conceive" of happening nevertheless had happened. It was thus ironic when the October 21, 1963, issue of *Clin-Alert,* a publication for physicians, noted that some recent experiments showed that MER/29 caused cataracts in rats and commented that it was "unfortunate, to say the least, that the present report, or one comparable to it, was not available before MER/29 was employed clinically." Merrell, of course, knew as early as 1960 that MER/29 might cause cataracts in dogs. They knew of the Merck study in January 1961. They were informed of one human cataract case in February 1961, at which time Merrell's librarian was asked to research the incidence of cataracts in humans. Yet the company sat on their suspicions until October 1961 when the unimpeachable Mayo Clinic reported that two patients receiving MER/29 had developed cataracts after first undergoing hair and skin changes.

Why Merrell sat on all of this information for so long is a question that has never been satisfactorily answered; just as no one is quite sure why Kevadon was not removed from the Canadian market or from the cabinets of the clinical investigators in this country until almost four months after Chemie Grünenthal and its British licensee recalled their brands of thalidomide. The answer may lie in that human affliction which Arthur Koestler in the *Act of Creation* called intellectual "snowblindness": the inability to perceive, because of the glare of expectations or hopes, things as they really are. In Merrell's case, this glare was undoubtedly intensified by the expectation of enormous profits. This intellectual snowblindness is akin to what Judge Friendly described as the "human tendency to follow a course of conduct once decided upon," a tendency "particularly strong when large investments of both effort and money have been made."

Thus, I have been told, Merrell's initial reaction when they learned of the Merck study was that the competing drug company was just trying to wreck what was developing as Merrell's most profitable product. Similarly, in a memorandum recounting the February 21, 1961, meeting with the Food and

Drug Administration, Merrell's Dr. Bunde could report that
he had "a very strong impression" that the FDA did not
consider MER/29 to be toxic, but merely ineffective. In
February 1962, one month before they would withdraw the
drug, Merrell could reassure Canadian physicians that there
was "still no positive proof" that thalidomide was causing
birth defects, and Getman testified that he still had his doubts
as to whether MER/29 caused the cataracts or the other
side effects which were attributed to it.

Merrell's inability to recognize the flaws in MER/29 even
after they were clearly visible to others is but one cause of
the MER/29 tragedy. Another was given by federal district
Judge Mathew M. McGuire when he passed sentence on the
companies and the three individual defendants. "I have taken
the view," he said, "that responsibility in the background of
this case is a failure, for want of a better term, of proper
managerial and supervisional control."

Merrell's president, Frank N. Getman, and vice-presidents,
with the exception of Dr. Werner, were neither physicians nor
scientists. They accordingly could exercise little control over
the scientific affairs of the company, the sole business of
which was the manufacturing and marketing of complex pharmaceutical products. Getman and his management associates
had to rely almost entirely on subordinates who were scientifically trained. More often than not, these subordinates
were under constant pressure from their "lay" superiors, for
whom scientific realities were secondary to business needs,
to develop new products in limited periods of time. The
temptation must have been very great for them to squash
a bug here and there, as they knew that the accuracy or
completeness of their scientific reports could not be questioned.

The following excerpts from Getman's pre-trial testimony
illustrate his lack of direct control over the scientific affairs
of his company:

> A: . . . Scientific papers I don't understand. So I scan them
> or read a summary.
> Q: How about reports?

A: Departmental reports that went over my desk, some-times open sometimes not.

Q: Sometimes open and sometimes not?

A: Sometimes open and sometimes not.

Q: I don't understand what you mean by not open.

A: A lot of these reports went over my desk and I didn't open the cover, the volume. At other times, I opened it to get an impression of the fields in which we were working in these departments.

❖　❖　❖

Q: When you received the data from the Merck company which was requested by Dr. Werner, was that submitted to the FDA?

A: I don't know the things that were submitted to the FDA by my company.

Q: Before anything was submitted to the FDA didn't it pass over your desk?

A: No.

Q: Wasn't it necessary for all data to be submitted to the FDA to be first shown to you?

A: No.

Q: Did you permit others to prepare information, data, forms' applications for submission to the FDA without your approving it or seeing it?

A: Yes, that was their job.

Q: Did you have any method by which the data to be sub-mitted to the Food and Drug Administration be checked by somebody or approved by somebody?

Mr. Nolan [attorney for Richardson-Merrell]: At this point, in the light of the various charges that have been made in the pending indictment, I am going to object to the question and direct the witness not to answer.

❖　❖　❖

Q: When did you make the decision to submit the new drug application for MER/29?

A: I didn't make it.

Q: Didn't you join in the decision to have this new drug application put together?

A: No. I was advised when it was ready.

Q: Did you see any parts of the new drug application before it was in final form?

Mr. Nolan: I think I am going to interpose my objection to this question. We are getting into the area that at least so far as the biological sciences area is concerned is within the scope of the indictment. Now, to the extent of asking Mr. Getman about any other areas of the new drug application, I would have no objection to that.

Q: Who made the decision then, to submit the new drug application?

A: I never thought of it in terms of decision-making. When it is ready, it is submitted, when the work is complete.

Q: Doesn't somebody have to make a decision or give an order concerning the filing of a new drug application or is this just routine with your company, with the William S. Merrell Company?

Mr. Nolan: Again, I am going to object to testimony with respect to procedures followed by the company with respect to the submission of a new drug application. I think it is sufficiently close to the subject matter of the pending criminal proceeding so as to warrant my raising my previous objection and direction.

❖   ❖   ❖

Q: At the time that the new drug application was made, did the company believe that its clinical tests were complete enough so that if the Government immediately cleared the drug for marketing, the company would have marketed it?

A: No, we did not. The company contemplated added clinical work prior to marketing.

❖   ❖   ❖

Q: If you thought it was not desirable for marketing, why did you make the new drug application at that time?

A: As I told you earlier, all I can say is that, apparently, in the judgment of our Medical Research Department, the evidence was adequate to meet the requirements of the law. If it were not, the Government would so advise us.

❖   ❖   ❖

Q: After the drug went on the market, did the Merrell Company have any means or system for keeping the clinical investigators who were still working with the

      drug informed and up to date on the latest results being
      experienced with the use of the drug?

A: Once again, you are asking questions about details, or if
      they are not details, regular procedures of our Medical
      Research Department with which I personally am not
      familiar.

*   *   *

Q: Were full reports of all clinical investigations that had
      been made to show whether or not the drug was safe
      for use furnished to the Food and Drug Administration?

A: I did not read nor have I read the company's new drug
      application, so I am just not in a position to answer your
      question. I might add nor do I know all of the clinical
      work that was done with the drug.

When asked whether he thought it was wise to have pharmaceutical companies under the direction of men not able to
fully evaluate the complex scientific and medical developments in their business, Getman replied that he did think
so. "No person," he explained, "is able to answer all of the
questions that arise, and the president's job is to have an
organization which is equipped to handle this type of question." The pleas of Merrell and three of their scientists to
the grand jury's indictment indicate that Getman's organization was evidently not so "equipped."

    Not only was he unfamiliar with the scientific details of
his company's operation, but Getman was unable to devote
his full time to Merrell's affairs. In the summer of 1959, when
the MER/29 New Drug Application was filed, he was made
the chairman of the management committee of Hess and
Clark, a Richardson-Merrell subsidiary which manufactures
veterinary drugs. In 1960 he was made Hess and Clark's president and general manager. In February 1961, a date which
marks the beginning of MER/29's most critical period,
Getman became executive vice-president of Richardson-
Merrell and was given responsibility for yet another subsidiary, the National Drug Company. He testified that at that
time his "initial objective was to spend all the time" he could

learning about his new corporate charge. Thus when he was asked, "So, from 1959 until 1962 or the end of 1961, you did not have much time to devote to the problems of the William S. Merrell Company?" he replied, "I had time. I did devote time, but a portion of my time." Getman characterized the portion as being "significant," but also admitted that there "would be periods, for example a week, when I might spend 90% of my time on Merrell, and other weeks when I spent none."

Although Richardson-Merrell would not permit me to interview any of their officers or employees (their attorneys did graciously supply me with many of the documents which had been previously given to the grand jury and the MER/29 Group, however), a partner in their Wall Street law firm, during the course of a free-flowing five-hour discussion, attempted to vindicate the company's actions. He argued that "whether or not mistakes were made," Merrell's management acted "in good faith" in making the "very difficult decisions as to the significance of various findings at various times."

While it was possible, the attorney conceded, "to look at isolated bits and pieces" of the MER/29 story "and say 'Gee, this could have been done a little bit better, or that could have been done, or maybe this memorandum isn't worded in the best possible way,'" he argued that the "major decisions" were correctly made. As an example, what he called Merrell's "big management decision" was the one to mail a warning letter to physicians after the company learned of the two Mayo cataract cases. "At the time," he stressed, "there was no pussy-footing around, there was no delay." He excoriated the Food and Drug Administration for demanding that Merrell's draft of the warning letter be rewritten (Dr. Nestor, the medical officer then in charge of the MER/29 NDA, had contended that Merrell's proposed drafts were "inadequate, weak, and might serve to mislead rather than help"), arguing that this prevented the company from immediately advising doctors to discontinue the drug if hair and skin reactions developed. This delay, he charged, was "a classic example of how a bureaucratic organization trying to act in the public interest can, in effect, hurt the public interest."

When asked about the discrepancies between what was observed in Merrell's laboratories and what was reported to the FDA, the attorney insisted that many were insignificant and added that the "dog cataracts that apparently occurred in the spring of 1960," as far as he knew, "never got outside the laboratory." Certainly, he concluded, "there was no intent, no design, to conceal or deceive the FDA or anybody else."

> It seems to me, that if you look at it, a drug company like Merrell, that's been in operation, well Merrell itself since 1828, Richardson-Merrell, Vick, since some time in the latter part of the nineteenth century, they've been in business for a long time, they've got a company with many thousand employees, many millions of dollars in sales every year. They aren't—there is no reason for them to "make a fast buck" by putting out a dangerous drug. It just doesn't make any sense.

When asked about Merrell's aborted venture with Kevadon, the lawyer again denied that the company had done anything improper:

> Whatever may be said about Merrell's conduct in connection with MER/29, you can argue that back and forth, or whether Beulah Jordan was right or wrong, or whether the Merck study should have tipped them off, or [Dr. Corday's patient] or what, whatever you say there, on the thalidomide, Kevadon side, this company was just a victim of some pretty bizarre and grotesque and tragic circumstances, both not only for it but for the people taking this [drug]. It was a sad and shocking experience because these people aren't gnomes sitting out there in the laboratory trying to figure out "what can we foist on the market." They're basically decent, honorable, careful guys who are called upon to make judgments as to the significance of information. And sometimes, you make the wrong judgment.

An interesting sidelight to the MER/29 affair was that

both Merrell president Getman and Dr. Van Maanen (who was indicted for falsifying information submitted to the FDA) testified that they took MER/29 until it was withdrawn from the market in April 1962. Merrell's chief scientist, Dr. Werner, who was similarly indicted by the federal grand jury, also testified that he took MER/29. When asked why, he replied, "Just because it was a new drug we had and I didn't have to pay for it and that is basically the reason why." When asked if he took all of Merrell's new drugs, he answered, "No, but I try quite a few of them if I think there is any reason for me to. It is good experience." Dr. Werner, who is not a physician, then admitted that he did not take MER/29 for a long period of time because his physician had not recommended it.

Apparently none of the three suffered any ill effects.

Postscript

The MER/29 and thalidomide tragedies brought needless suffering to many people. Merrell's story is not unique. Too many pharmaceutical products have had to be withdrawn from the market because of inadequacies in their testing and manufacture.

Before I left the richly appointed offices of Richardson-Merrell's Wall Street lawyers, I was assured that Merrell, aware of prior mistakes, "has gone to great pains" to guarantee that "barring human error, their submissions to the Food and Drug Administration will be complete and accurate in every way." This, of course, will be helpful, as were the 1962 Kefauver-Harris amendments to the food and drug laws. Passed over the strenuous objections of the pharmaceutical industry, they have given the FDA some of its much needed power to protect us. More, however, needs to be done. Briefly, I think this short history of one drug company's problems underscores the need for the following reforms:

1. New drugs are needed, and research must continue. However, they must be thoroughly tested before being released for general sale (whether by prescription or over the counter). This testing should be under the strict and direct supervision of either the government or an independent group with no financial stake in the test results.
2. The totality of a drug company's experience with a drug (excluding, of course, bona fide trade secrets) must be made available to any interested person. A physician cannot properly balance the risks of a certain treatment

against its expected benefits unless he has all the information. "Puffing," the business euphemism for fraudulent advertising, must not be permitted.

The drug is a potent two-edged sword. It can do much good, but it can also do much harm. The proper use of drugs has relegated many of the scourges of past ages to the shadows of history; their improper use has brought injury and death. Implementation of the two procedures suggested above will do much to prevent further drug-caused tragedies.

New laws and procedures, however, are only part of the solution. Vigorous enforcement of those we now have—putting the drug companies to their proof—would go a long way toward solving the problem. Unfortunately the FDA, like other regulatory agencies, is under strong pressure to conform to the dictates of the industry it regulates. Because of mobility between commerce and government, some individuals try to remain on good terms with the companies which may one day be their employers. Two examples come readily to mind. The first concerns MER/29.

On December 1, 1959, Dr. F. Joseph Murray, Merrell's liaison with the Food and Drug Administration, informed the company's chief scientist that Dr. Jerome Epstein, the medical officer to whom the MER/29 New Drug Application was originally assigned, was leaving the agency. Dr. Epstein was, he wrote, "responsible for many of the concessions made" by the FDA, and Murray declared that he had been "counting heavily on his support" in getting the MER/29 application approved.

> I called Dr. Epstein and learned that his resignation becomes effective December 4. He does not know who will take over the 29 application. He is going into private practice in Washington and volunteered to intercede for us in any way possible at the time of our resubmission [of the MER/29 NDA]. I appreciate this and will certainly call on him if it appears desirable, but I am frankly skeptical as to how much good he can do us once he has left the FDA.

A more recent example of what Congressman Benjamin S. Rosenthal of New York has called the "in-and-out incestuousness of government and industry" is the resignation of FDA general counsel William Goodrich in May, 1971, to become president of the Institute of Shortening and Edible Oils, a trade association which has extensive dealings with the Food and Drug Administration. Mr. Goodrich's successor at the FDA is Peter Hutt, a Washington lawyer who has listed the trade association as one of his clients.

Without questioning the motives of Mr. Goodrich or Mr. Hutt, it is clear that the proper enforcement of laws designed to protect the public interest depends on the willingness of the enforcers to forgo subsequent employment in the regulated industry. Serious consideration should be given to "conflict of interest" legislation which would make this willingness a prerequisite to government employment.

Government control over the drug industry, no matter how strict the rules are or how vigorously they are enforced, will be ineffective unless the prevailing attitudes of that industry are changed. In 1966 Dr. James L. Goddard, then commissioner of the Food and Drug Administration, reported that he was dismayed that drug companies were still being less than candid in their submissions. "I have been shocked," he told an annual meeting of the Pharmaceutical Manufacturers Association, "at the materials that come in to us. I have been shocked at the clear attempts to slip something by us. I am deeply disturbed at the constant, direct, personal pressure some industry representatives have placed on our people." Dr. Goddard charged that in their haste to show a profit for their stockholders, many drug companies had lost sight of their ultimate social function:

> Gentlemen, we must keep our eyes on the patient. For— once you get through the medical reports and the counselors' opinions, the advertising and the marketing data, the licensing and distribution agreements, the protocols and letters of credit, the labeling and packaging, and the reports by the

company treasurer—once you get through all that, you reach the physician who will administer your product to a human being.

At the end of the long line is a human life. Some of you seem to have forgotten this basic fact.

The following case illustrates the continuing validity of Dr. Goddard's indictment and the need for reform:

Early in 1971 an epidemic of a sometimes fatal blood poisoning in hospitalized patients was traced to the bottles of intravenous fluids (those hanging affairs which feed nutrient solutions directly into the patient's bloodstream) manufactured by Abbott Laboratories, one of the nation's largest pharmaceutical concerns (at the time of the epidemic they were supplying some 45 percent of the intravenous fluids used in this country). In March, Dennis Maki, a thirty-one-year-old physician with the Public Health Service's Center for Disease Control, discovered the source of the trouble: Abbott's bottle-cap liners were contaminated by the disease-causing bacteria. This information was immediately presented to Abbott. At a March 11 meeting with government health officials the company not only disclaimed responsibility for the contamination of their solutions (hospital personnel bang the caps, they charged, causing the fluid to come in contact with the liners) but, according to the respected professional newsletter *Drug Research Reports*, actually contended that they had "never made sterility claims" for the cap liners. On March 22, after public prodding by Ralph Nader, the Food and Drug Administration recalled Abbott's intravenous fluids.

A Center for Disease Control survey of eight out of 8,000 hospitals known to have used Abbott fluids revealed 150 cases of blood poisoning, including nine deaths. The true toll can only be guessed at. They are the victims of a system which all too often places profit and prestige above the patient; a system which must be changed.

Index